# My Secret Loss

# My Secret Loss

## Finding Peace after Abortion

Sheila M. Luck

Visit Sheila's website: www.icanwithiam.com

*My Secret Loss* – Sheila M. Luck



First edition published 2005



Cover Design: Kim West, M.Div., Ph.D. (New Heart Solutions)

*Editor: Sheila Wilkinson*

Printed in the United States of America

www.anekopress.com

Life Sentence Publishing books are available at
discounted prices for ministries and other outreach.
Find out more by contacting us at info@lspbooks.com

Life Sentence Publishing, and its logo are trademarks of

Life Sentence Publishing, Inc.
P.O. Box 652
Abbotsford, WI 54405

**FAMILY & RELATIONSHIPS / Death, Grief, Bereavement**

Paperback ISBN: 978-1-62245-003-9

Ebook ISBN: 978-1-62245-004-6

10 9 8 7 6 5 4 3 2 1

Available wherever books are sold.

Share this book on Facebook:

# Contents

Scan to watch a video by Sheila Luck

# Acknowledgements

Only through the support and encouragement of many others has this work been made possible. I thank you all with deepest gratitude.

Specifically, I'd like to thank my husband, Wayne, for his love and constant reassurances that writing this and related works are worthwhile endeavors. He never lets me give up, and he helps me with many ideas along the way.

I'd also like to thank my daughters, Chelsy and Krista. I'm afraid my conversations have become somewhat narrowly focused for the past several months. But they listened supportively along every step. Most importantly, however, without their continued love and understanding after learning of my past mistakes, this work would not be possible. God has shown his love for me through them. I am forever grateful.

Continuing with my family members, my sister Jill Loken has patiently walked with me as I traveled along on my faith journey, occasionally leading, occasionally prodding, often encouraging, and frequently waiting as I slowly caught on to God's will for my life. She has listened to my various stories, over and over, always with love, understanding, and encouragement, as only a sister can do.

A number of friends have generously devoted their time to tell me their stories and experiences or to read and critique various versions of this workbook, lending me both their professional knowledge and their thoughts based on their own experiences. Their stories, comments, and questions have been invaluable. While I have had conversations with many friends, I specifically want to thank my friend Colleen Hansen, my friend and confidant Pastor Vicki Fink, and a new friend with substantial experience leading women's Bible study groups, Kim Owens. Thank you all very much for your time, your suggestions and your encouragement.

Many friends helped influence the final cover design through email and Facebook messages, providing insight as to feelings and impressions invoked by a variety of design ideas. Ultimately, Dr. Kim West of New Heart Solutions volunteered her time to create a pictorial design that I believe provides a sense of peace. This design creates for me a vision of the place I want to be: a place of warmth and safety, a place filled with Jesus' love, and a place filled with loving thoughts of my baby lost. This is also the place to which I pray all readers of this workbook will reach.

I'd like to thank Kelly Hawkins and Scott Stewart of Silas Publishing (later named CarePoint Ministry) for giving me my first publishing opportunity, Silas Publishing being the first to publish this workbook.

Finally, many thanks are owed to Jeremiah Zeiset of Life Sentence Publishing and his team of professionals, who enabled this workbook to be updated and republished. Although there are several people involved with the many publication steps, I wish to specially thank Amber Burger for her patience with me as I struggled to define for her just the right look for the cover design.

I pray that all people using this workbook will find peace through Jesus, our Great Healer and Redeemer.

Introduction

# Using this Workbook

This workbook has been written for all who have dealt with a crisis pregnancy, either directly or indirectly, which ended in abortion. Perhaps you personally had an abortion and are struggling with the consequences of your loss. Maybe you have a daughter or mother who is struggling with the emotional pain and guilt of a past abortion.

This book is designed to be used in a small group study; however, it can also be used as a personal workbook.

As a small group study, it's possible to finish the workbook in ten weekly meetings. However, if your group is able to schedule twelve meetings, I encourage you to do so. The first week should then be devoted to reading the introductory materials and getting to know each other. The last week should be reserved for schedule slippage, allowing extra time so the group isn't pressed by the schedule if it's in the middle of a meaningful conversation.

If only ten weekly meetings are scheduled for your small group, each participant is encouraged to read the introductory materials and my personal story in the beginning of the workbook prior to the first meeting.

The rest of the workbook is divided into ten weekly discussion sections. Within each week's materials, my story is written to serve as a backdrop for the particular week's topic, and it's followed by related discussion questions. Through either my story or the discussion questions, you may recognize yourself, your friend, your mother, or your daughter. By beginning each weekly discussion section with my personal story, I have tried to enable even the most uncomfortable group members to actively participate in the group. You can discuss the weekly topics in terms of my story if you do not wish to share your own story with the group.

Following the section related to my personal story, each chapter includes a brief Bible study intended to help you and the group participants relate God's Word to the topic being discussed for the week. Through his Word, I pray you will find peace, a peace only he can give.

There are homework questions at the end of each weekly section. These enable you to delve deeper into your personal experiences in the privacy of your home. During each subsequent week, you will be given the opportunity to share with the group what you may have learned through the homework exercises, although such sharing is not required.

For some of you, discussing openly the circumstances of your own abortion might be too hard. For those who are using this workbook to gain a better understanding of your friend or family member who has had an abortion, you may not have sufficient details to participate with your own examples. Therefore, I have tried to draft the discussion questions in a way that will allow you to reflect on your own or known circumstances; but, if needed, discuss your thoughts in terms of my circumstances or in general terms.

From time to time, you might find the discussion too painful for your active participation in the small group. It is okay to silently listen, reflect, and pray. But I encourage you to remember that you are not alone, and you need not work through these issues alone. Allow God to lead you. Allow him to open your heart, your mind, and your memory. The path may be difficult at times, but trust him to be with you on every step.

If you are using this workbook as a personal workbook, you will find spots at the beginning of each section that are intended to encourage discussion within a small group. These ice-breaker questions can be skipped. Also, as you try to answer the discussion questions, you'll notice that the answers can be found in the reading material just before each question. I tried to enable readers to work through the workbook independently; a group leader should not be needed to answer the questions.

Finally, please recognize that I am not a professional counselor and this workbook cannot take the place of professional counseling. However, it is my belief that women can and should be encouraged and supported through the understanding and compassion of other women, particularly those who have faced similar circumstances. Encouraging one another, woman to woman, is a natural part of God's plan. After years of walking alone and trying to carry the myriad of emotions from my past abortion, I finally sought God's helping hand. With extensive Bible study and prayer, I worked through the many questions that I pose to you in this workbook, particularly those listed in the homework exercises. Through this personal reflection and Bible study, made possible by God's everlasting presence, mercy, grace, and forgiveness, I have found peace.

By my discussion of the paths leading to an unintended pregnancy, abortion, denial, attempts to escape the memories, and ultimately finding peace in God's love, I hope the doors for understanding, compassion, and healing will open for you. However, please remember that for many of us full and complete healing can take a long time. God will open new doors for you only when you are ready to handle each new door and not before.

If you want to pursue additional reading or other resources, I encourage you to consider some of the resources noted in Appendix A.

For some of you, especially those with symptoms that are debilitating, seriously harmful to your health or well-being, or interfering with your ability to work or manage your day-to-day activities, I urge you to seek help from a pastoral or professional, Christian counselor. Please call your church office for a referral to an appropriate member of the pastoral staff or to a licensed professional Christian counselor.

> *So there is hope for your future, declares the Lord.*
> Jeremiah 31:17a

## Post-Abortion Stress: What Is It?

Having had an abortion is often a woman's deepest secret. She may be afraid to tell her family, friends, or others who are close to her out of fear of retribution or condemnation. Meeting people with compassion for her and an understanding of the circumstances surrounding her choice is rarely expected. As she hears and sees much of today's pro-life propaganda, she is confronted not only with the declaration that her choice was wrong, but that she is personally unacceptable, unforgivable, or unworthy. On occasion, the woman might finally confide in a trusted friend, only to be rebuked and shamed by her friend.

Many women feel guilty about their decision. Some discover later that the information they were given was not fully accurate. They now know that they aborted a baby, not just tissue as they may have been told. Some women knew at the time of their abortion that the decision conflicted with either God's will or their personal morals and beliefs, but they found themselves reluctantly agreeing to the procedure anyway. Maybe they were taken to the clinic by their parents, their boyfriend, or someone else who insisted that an abortion was the best solution. Some women were forced into an abortion, completely against their will. Now, in the aftermath, they struggle terribly.

Not only do women feel guilt after an abortion, but they often find they have been unable to cope with their feelings of loss and grief. An aborted baby is a woman's secret loss. No forum exists for them to grieve – no funeral, no gravesite, and no memorial. Women are frequently unable to talk to family or friends about their loss and resultant grief, because they don't know how to explain grief over a loss they chose through abortion.

Again, all of these women risk facing a lack of sympathy or empathy; or worse, they risk facing ridicule and judgment. Often, when they try to bring up the subject, well-meaning friends or family tell them to forget about it and move on. "It's over," they remind her. So, these women conclude it is best to carry their grief and feelings of guilt in secret. The abortion is their secret loss, a loss with none of the usual support structures for healing and recovery.

The evil forces of this world work to pull us away from God and his will for our lives. Thus, one can be sure that Satan (believed by many to be a fallen angel and believed by others to be the personification of all evil forces) is thrilled that we try to carry the burdens resulting from our abortions alone. Satan doesn't want us to find forgiveness for our past choices. He doesn't want us to share our losses with others.

He wants us to carry our guilt and grief all alone. By keeping us alone with our guilt and grief and by forcing us to suppress our many related feelings, he is able to control our lives, destroying our sense of worth and well-being.

Referring to Satan, it is written in the gospel of John that *the thief does not come except to steal, and to kill, and to destroy* (John 10:10a NKJV). With the goal to destroy our self-esteem, our self-confidence, our sense of worth, and ultimately our relationship with God, Satan continually reminds us of our prior choices, thereby driving his sword deeper and deeper into our hearts. Satan has been successful in his endeavors. However, while instances of rejection, rebuke, and condemnation from other people may occur, statistics show that women who have had abortions are clearly not alone.

The Alan Guttmacher Institute has estimated that "at current rates about 3 in 10 American women will have had an abortion by the time she reaches age 45." Their specific data indicates that more than 53 million legal abortions were performed in the United States between 1972 and 2011. The women choosing abortion come from all walks of life, economic brackets, educational backgrounds, marital circumstances, and religious affiliations. For example, 37% of women obtaining abortions consider themselves to be Protestant, and 28% identify themselves as Catholic. Sixty-one percent of women obtaining abortions already have one or more children. Forty-five percent of women choosing abortion have never married, and they were not living with a partner at the time of the abortion.[1]

While we read these statistics with sadness, they show us that it is likely that most American families have been affected by abortion in some manner. But how many of these women feel free to share their story? It is clearly not a topic for casual conversation. Most post-abortive women will never disclose to others that they have had an abortion, at least not beyond their closest circle of confidants. Many of these same women, in an attempt to keep their abortion a secret from all, will refuse to tell their spouses, their grown children, their parents or even

1 "Fact Sheet, Induced Abortion in the United States," July 2014, The Alan Guttmacher Institute, New York and Washington DC, 10 November 2014, *www.guttmacher.org/pubs/fb_induced_abortion.html.*

their doctors. There are many, many women who are carrying their burden alone. But we don't have to be alone. We can share our burden with others who have found themselves in similar circumstances, and we can help each other in the process of this sharing.

> *Carry each other's burdens,*
> *and in this way you will fulfill the law of Christ.*
> Galatians 6:2

As we suppress our guilt, grief, and fear of reprisal, the aftereffects of abortion are far-reaching – causing anxiety, sleep disturbances, aggressive behavior, difficulty concentrating, recurrent and intrusive thoughts of the abortion or the aborted child, flashbacks, withdrawal from relationships, a restricted ability to love or have tender feelings, sexual dysfunction, or depression, which may include thoughts of suicide. There may be feelings of unrelenting guilt, shame, inadequacy, intense grief, and anger or fits of rage. Some women may develop eating disorders, abuse alcohol or drugs, or practice other self-degrading or self-destructive behaviors. Yet others experience nightmares, imagine hearing babies crying, or see visions of infants calling to them.[2]

Post-abortion stress or post-abortion stress syndrome is the clinical name given to this myriad of emotions and physical or behavioral responses resulting from the trauma of an abortion. Some of these symptoms are severe, requiring professional intervention, while some symptoms might be managed in a more personal way. Still, in some situations, the symptoms might have developed so slowly over time that the resultant feelings of inadequacy, shyness, perfectionism, short temper, or insecurity have simply become part of the woman's personality.

For some women, these feelings surface within days or weeks following an abortion. For other women, the feelings lie dormant, surfacing years after the abortion, perhaps as she develops the painful recognition of the actual impact of abortion. Many women may face some of the symptoms or feelings but are unable to identify the connection to

2 David C. Reardon, "The After Effects of Abortion," 1990 Elliott Institute (text from a brochure), 14 January 2015, www.abortionfacts.com/reardon/the-after-effects -of-abortion

their abortion, having denied for so long that the abortion had any impact at all.[3]

To obtain an objective statistic regarding the percentage of women struggling with symptoms of post-abortion stress, studies will often look at the numbers of post-abortive women that have sought medical or psychological treatment. However, not all women seek medical or psychological help for the struggles they face. Some do not even realize that their struggles are related to their choice to have an abortion. This failure to recognize the tie to an abortion is often exacerbated by a reluctance and occasional refusal by some in the medical and counseling fields to recognize post-abortion stress as an actual emotional or psychological problem. Some professionals are afraid that by recognizing this as a real problem they will suddenly find themselves in the middle of the pro-life verses pro-choice battle.

For all of these reasons, it is difficult to determine the percentage of women who face or have faced symptoms that may be classified as post-abortion stress.

Post-abortion stress, regardless of the degree to which it has impacted your life, can be healed through God's grace through the death and resurrection of Jesus Christ. Likely, you will not find complete healing in ten short weeks of Bible study, but nothing is impossible for God. Although walking down this path may be very hard, keep a faithful heart and he will give you strength.

*So do not fear, for I am with you;*
*do not be dismayed, for I am your God.*
*I will strengthen you and help you;*
*I will uphold you with my righteous right hand.*
Isaiah 41:10

3 David C. Reardon, Ph.D., "A List of Major Psychological Complications of Abortion," 2011, The Elliot Institute, 14 January 2015, *www.afterabortion.org/2011/abortion-risks-a-list-of-major-psychological-complications-related-to-abortion.*

## My Secret Loss

# The Author's Story

*It is anticipated that this section will be read by small group participants on their own time.*

My husband and I have two lovely daughters, beautiful in every way; but, most importantly, they have beautiful hearts. They were both born in November. The oldest daughter was born on November 6th. She came into this world with a small tuft of auburn hair on the top of her head and dark bluish-brown eyes. She was born with God's perfect design, having all ten fingers and all ten toes and everything functioning in the proper way. I thought she was the most beautiful baby in the world. (Of course, every mother's baby is believed to be the most beautiful baby in the world.) I loved her totally with all of my heart right from the moment of her birth.

Our youngest daughter was born just a day before Thanksgiving. She too was the most beautiful baby in the whole world. As an infant, she had the tiniest amount of soft, strawberry-blonde, fuzzy hair, blonde eyebrows, and blue eyes. Just as with our first daughter, I loved our second daughter totally and instantaneously, even before her first whimper of breath.

Both daughters fill my heart with joy. They are blessings from God.

Our daughters are now twenty-seven and twenty-five years old. Throughout their childhood years, in November, they impatiently awaited their birthdays with excited anticipation. We would plan their birthday parties for weeks (and sometimes months) in advance. They'd invite all of their friends over. Sometimes they'd want a slumber party. Sometimes they'd choose to go to a kids play land. Sometimes we'd get a piñata filled with enough candy for everyone. Other times we'd fill party bags with candy and trinkets to give each of the kids. November, for our daughters, has always been one of the best months of the year.

But my memories of events in November are not all filled with joy. I remember another November long ago, several years before our daughters were born. In fact, it was about forty years ago now. This story of a very personal choice began at the beginning of November, near the birth date of my oldest daughter and ended near the birth date of my youngest daughter. How terribly ironic that such joyous events are forever clouded with my earlier choices.

I was seventeen years old. A couple weeks before Thanksgiving, although I don't remember the exact date, I borrowed a car from someone at school so I could go to a doctor's appointment. I had secretly called for the appointment when my mother wasn't home. The doctor I chose wasn't our normal family doctor. I didn't dare go to him. I went to a neighboring town, believing that my potential secret would be more secure there. I even borrowed a car from a classmate so my mother could not question me on my need for a car.

I didn't tell anyone where I was going. I didn't even tell the doctor's office the purpose of my visit, not until I was in the examining room.

"I think I might be pregnant," I said, afraid to look directly at the doctor or the nurse. The words seemed to hang in the air forever. "I missed two periods," I said in response to the doctor's questions.

I wanted desperately to escape that moment. I wished I could be back at school. I wished I had not made the choices I had made. I hoped my suspicions were wrong. Home pregnancy tests at that time were known to be unreliable. I guessed that I was pregnant based on my physical circumstances: a missed period or two, a daily upset stomach, and firmness in my lower abdomen.

Unfortunately, my suspicions were correct. I was pregnant, about eight weeks along based on the doctor's estimate. The baby was due to be born the following May. The doctor told me about my options. I could have the baby and either keep it or give it up for adoption. As an alternative, he mentioned that there was an abortion clinic located about an hour's drive away. He said that our state law required parental consent for abortions. "Why don't you go home and think about it. Talk to your parents," he said. "But decide within the next couple weeks. If you go beyond twelve weeks pregnant, abortion will not be an option, at least not in this state." He talked as though having an abortion was a perfectly normal, acceptable choice. It was simply another option.

I drove back to school, all the while wondering what I should do next and crying about the reality of my new circumstances. When I arrived at school, I quickly wiped my tears away before going inside, trying to gain my composure so no one would ask me what was wrong. I couldn't let anyone know. With a quiet word of thanks, I then returned the borrowed car keys to their rightful owner, hoping that no one could tell that I was pregnant.

After school and finally at home in the safety of my bedroom, I cried.

I had nowhere to go for help. I couldn't tell my mother. I believed that she would make me move out of the house. Where would I go? I couldn't live on my own. How would I support myself? How could I support a baby? I couldn't tell my school friends. I thought they would ridicule or abandon me. How could I tell my brothers or sister? I didn't know how they could help me. I couldn't let my secret out. I just knew that everyone in town would gossip about me. I heard them talk badly about other unwed, pregnant girls in the past. I assumed that I'd be the new focal point for their gossip. I was sure that no one would befriend me. I'd be alone, with nothing: no friends, no family, no home, and no ability to support myself.

I was alone and afraid with the biggest decision of my life.

*If I had the baby, could I keep it? How could I support a baby?* I wondered. *If my mother doesn't help me, I'll have no place to live. I haven't finished high school yet. How could I get a job that paid enough to support me and a baby? I can't even support just me.*

I cried and cried. The more I cried, the more devastated I became.

*Should I tell the father?* I wondered silently. *No*, I quickly decided. Even though I had hoped he loved me, I knew he did not. I believed that involving him would just add to my public humiliation. I believed that he'd refuse to stand by me in this situation.

I cried some more. I was alone and afraid. I had no way to support a baby. I didn't know where to turn.

I briefly contemplated suicide, but I believed there had to be a better solution. I couldn't take my own life. I didn't want to die.

I thought about going through with the pregnancy and giving the baby up for adoption. Believing that I couldn't continue to live at home, I didn't know where I'd live until the baby was born. I was planning to start college in January and live in the dorms. Would it be possible to keep my pregnancy a secret and simply live in the dorm as planned? No, I was certain that idea would not work. Who would want a pregnant roommate? Even if I could figure out where to live while I was pregnant, I couldn't picture giving the baby up for adoption.

I thought about having and keeping the baby. I thought that I could love a baby and take care of it – at least in my heart. I always dreamed of having children. Having a baby now would just be earlier than I planned. Of course, I always planned to be married first, and I knew that marriage was not an option in this case. As I continued to think about keeping the baby, every idea seemed impossible. My mind raced to find an answer.

I felt desperate for a solution.

Not knowing what I wanted to do for certain, I loaded my pockets with quarters and walked to a phone booth. I called someone I knew who lived in another state. After he answered, I tried to nonchalantly ask, "Can I come visit you?" I didn't tell him why I wanted to visit. I couldn't seem to say it out loud. I couldn't face it. But somehow I thought that this friend could help. I was relieved to know someone I thought I could trust with my problems.

I walked home, deep in my thoughts.

Once at home, I locked myself in my bedroom. I didn't want my mom to see me. I was afraid she'd notice I was upset. I didn't want her to ask any questions. She was always asking questions. I wasn't prepared to tell her why I wanted to visit my friend. I needed time to create a plausible explanation. Then I could talk to her. Of course, I wouldn't tell her the truth.

I was so scared. I was so very alone.

Shortly before visiting my out-of-state friend, I wrote a letter to him to tell him I was pregnant. I didn't seek his advice in the letter. I simply concluded that abortion was my only option. "Besides, it's just tissue growing in my body at this time," I wrote in justification of my decision. I told him that an abortion would be a much smaller problem than going through with the pregnancy and being ostracized by my family, friends, and everyone I knew. "Abortion is the only possible option. I don't really have a choice," I wrote. I asked him to help me; then I mailed the letter.

A few days later, I met my friend and we drove to his apartment, making small talk along the way. He didn't ask why I wanted so badly to visit, and he didn't mention my letter. Maybe he thought I'd speak up sooner or later. I often kept quiet, not talking until the time seemed right. It was hard for me to trust anyone with matters of my heart.

At his apartment, my friend stepped out for a moment to get his mail. It took him a very long time to get his mail. I didn't realize that my letter had just arrived in his mailbox. He read it before he came back inside.

My mind was made up. I don't know if he agreed with my decision or not. I didn't ask for his opinion. I just asked him to help me do it – help me find a doctor and help me keep this pregnancy a secret forever. I didn't need money for the procedure; at least I didn't think so. I had money with me. I believed it was enough, although I wasn't sure how much an abortion cost.

After a few phone calls, we learned that parental consent was not required in this state; I could afford the procedure, and I could get an appointment while I was in town. My friend made the appointment for me, and he drove me to the clinic.

The drive to the clinic seemed to take forever. Maybe it was due to the lack of conversation. Maybe it was simply a long drive. It was a big city, and everything seemed far away to me. I wished my friend would talk more. He seemed kind of quiet.

The clinic was rather nondescript. It was in an office building. We rode up the elevator, found the right floor, walked down the hall, and opened a plain door to a waiting room. The waiting room seemed to have too many chairs for the size of the room; but there weren't too many chairs for the number of people in the room. Maybe there were about thirty straight-backed chairs, lined up side by side, using every available spot. Most seats were filled, being used by people who looked silently at their magazines, their hands, their feet, or the floor. They weren't talking. A particular sadness filled the air, although I didn't fully understand it. I didn't know there was anything to be concerned about. I didn't know that what I was doing might be wrong. It was legal, so it must be perfectly acceptable to resolve my problem in this way. I was so very naïve. I was so very young.

We found two vacant seats. I then tentatively went up to the window to check in. A few pairs of eyes glanced up to watch. I paid the office about three hundred dollars in cash. Cash was required. The receptionist gave me a form to complete. I sat back down, hoping it would be over soon.

"Do you want general anesthesia or local anesthesia?" That was the first question that I recall hearing after my name was called, and I walked nervously through the door to a consultation room.

"What's the difference?" I asked. I chose the risk of hallucinations upon waking from the general anesthesia over the awareness of a tugging sensation that I'd feel with a local anesthetic. It sounded awful either way, so I decided it would be best to be asleep. Today, I'm so thankful for that part of my decision.

My thoughts rambled and raced and rambled again, generally repeating everything the clinic had told me. It'll be over in a couple hours. Good thing I am here early, while it is still just tissue. I'll be asleep so I won't feel anything other than some cramping later. After I wake up, I'll feel like I am having my period. It's an easy procedure. Rarely are there complications. I might hallucinate as I wake up from the anesthesia, but there is nothing to worry about. Soon it'll be over and I can go back to school as though nothing happened.

My heart appreciated having a solution. I felt relief. I didn't seem to understand or believe that being pregnant meant a baby was already well-formed, taking shape and growing inside of me. I understood and thought only about my need to resolve my problem. It seemed to me that I was just taking care of a health problem. I needed to solve this problem, and abortion was the best way to do it. It was my only feasible option.

*It's not a baby yet*, I thought. *Besides, women now have the right to choose when to have a child. We don't have to have a baby until we are ready. Abortion is legal. It would be illegal if it was not an acceptable solution*, I reasoned to myself. *It'll all be over soon. I'll be able to go home; and no one will know a thing. I won't have to worry about it anymore.*

The needle looked so very long. The nurse stuck it in my arm, and I was soon asleep.

As I woke up, I hallucinated just as I was forewarned. I believed that my arms and legs were deformed, and I couldn't make them move in a normal manner. I was nauseous. I suddenly became very frightened! "Help! Help me! Help me! What did they do to me?" I cried out in fear and anguish.

"Shhhh!" was the stern reply. "It's just the medicine. You're fine. It's over."

They released me to go home. I was physically fine. The pregnancy was terminated, but it wasn't really over.

The drive back to my friend's apartment was longer than the drive to the clinic, or so it seemed. I tried to talk to my friend. I wanted to talk about what happened, and how I felt. I wanted to talk about what the nurses and the doctor said, how the procedure was described, and how I hallucinated when I woke up. Before I could say much of anything though, my friend interrupted, curtly saying, "I don't want to hear about it. I never want to talk about it."

What was that tone? Had I done something wrong? With a compliant attitude and a little confusion, I stopped talking about it. I decided then that I could never talk about it, to anyone. Maybe something was wrong with this choice. Was it wrong to end a pregnancy? The situation, I began to discover, was more than simply hiding from others the fact that I had gotten pregnant. But what exactly was the problem?

I was left alone with my thoughts and my questions and my confusion. I was left alone with my feelings, alone with my secret, and alone with my loss. This fateful November was to be my secret. It would always be my secret. I could let no one know, ever.

I went home, alone.

I thought I'd feel happy and satisfied with myself. I had solved my problem and no one knew about it. But I didn't feel the way I expected. I knew I had made many choices I wanted no one to know about. These choices involved unsatisfying relationships, an unintended pregnancy, and my ultimate choice to have an abortion.

How did I get on that path? All I wanted was to be accepted. I wanted friends. I wanted someone to love me. I wanted to wear his class ring. I wanted to get married. I wanted to live happily ever after, just like in the storybooks.

Instead, I took many wrong turns. The wrong turns were not made with loose morals or bad intentions. They were not made with an attitude of rebellion or free abandonment. I was just looking for love in the wrong places and from the wrong sources. Looking back, I realize I was looking for love along an independent path, a path upon which I did not understand the true source of love that can fill our every need. I didn't know that the foundation of all love was a relationship with God.

Searching for love without God's love as my foundation, I went down a very regrettable path. Like wading in the ocean waves, I found myself in too deep. The events surrounded me and pulled me further and further away from my childhood dreams and into a desperate situation. Fighting for a safe return to shore, I made the only choice I believed would save my life. My choice got my feet back on shore, but it did not give me my life, at least not as I had hoped.

I have since discovered it is impossible to escape the consequences of some choices. There is no running from them. There is no hiding from them. The consequences live on forever. They follow you throughout time, bringing guilt, shame, insecurity, pain, remorse, or grief. Success does not shake or destroy these feelings. New relationships, love of family and friends, marriage, and children do not change the past. With some choices, the consequences live on forever.

As I held my infant daughter in my arms about twelve years after that fateful November, watching the angelic halo form over her head as she slept, I thought about my first baby.

Was it a boy or a girl? Assuming it was a boy, I'd try to picture what he might have looked like and how tall he would be. I'd wonder whether he would have liked sports. Maybe he would have liked basketball, like my brother. Maybe he would have liked track, like me. Maybe he would have taken music lessons, playing the drums, a horn, or even the piano.

These thoughts continue to meander through my heart from time to time, over and over. Sometimes I'd picture a daughter instead of a son. Each time, I'd tell myself to just forget it. It's over. It was long ago. Instead of forgetting, I began to realize that I had missed so much. Through our daughters, I realized that all children are a blessing from God, whether or not we think we are ready for their expected arrival.

Through my choices, I have lost so much, especially through the choice that remains my darkest secret. I cannot share this loss with anyone. The child is gone forever. Who would understand that I could miss this child or mourn his or her loss, the loss of someone I didn't know I wanted in the first place? Who would believe I might grieve the loss of this child?

Grief never really goes away. Throughout life, there are continual reminders of the loss, things that cause us to think about what might have been but for the loss. Once reminded, sadness returns. Grief returns. Sometimes it is for just a moment. Sometimes it brings tears of lost days and lost opportunities. For me, the grief is just beginning and seems to grow in intensity as my understanding of the loss and its impact are more fully understood.

An old cliché says, "Time heals all wounds." It's not true. I know time does not heal the pain created by the loss of a loved one. Sometimes, as in my case, time must pass before the wound can open for the first time. Then, with God's healing touch, you learn to live with the loss. Life then becomes different, somehow better.

There is only one source for healing. Only through God's grace and his merciful forgiveness through his Son, Jesus Christ, have my wounds begun to heal. Time is not the source for healing, but God may use time to prepare your heart.

My story is not over, but it is a story of God's love and forgiveness. It is a story of hope. I know today that I am his daughter. He is my Abba, my daddy, my father. He is here with me every day. He has forgiven me.

I took the long route to find peace after my abortion, about thirty years of life's travels. It took me so long because I didn't understand the path existed or how to find it. I also didn't understand that being on God's path could actually change things. Yet, each day, I discover new signs of God's love, acceptance, forgiveness, reconciliation, and healing. Even as I write, I find myself going back to amend my story with new discoveries or memories or feelings that God has brought forth in my heart.

A while ago, my husband and I went to the town in which I graduated from high school to visit my brother and his wife. At one time, I enjoyed going back to my hometown. But over the years my attitude changed as I tried to bury painful memories. For twenty years, I really didn't want to return to that town. When we'd visit my brother, I'd be afraid I'd run into someone from high school. I really didn't want to see them and risk having to face the memories again. Worse yet, what if they remembered something that I did not want to be remembered anymore?

A recent visit was different though. When I ran into an old high school friend, I unexpectedly discovered I was happy to see her. We enjoyed reminiscing over old stories. For the first time in years, I didn't hate the memories. I was no longer afraid of the memories. I realized I didn't need to hide from my past, but I also knew I didn't need to advertise it. It is still my secret loss, but I have a loving, heavenly Father with whom I can share it. I know, too, that even if my past becomes known and is met with disdain or an unwillingness to recognize that God has forgiven me, I am forgiven. I know emphatically that my slate is wiped clean and God loves me. No one will, nor can they ever, change that fact. That knowledge, which comes by faith, gives me strength.

> *For I am convinced that neither death nor life, neither angels nor demons, neither the present nor the future, nor any powers, neither height nor depth, nor anything else in all creation, will be able to separate us from the love of God that is in Christ Jesus our Lord.* Romans 8:38-39

That day, when meeting my old friend from high school, I discovered that God removed Satan's lies from my heart, the lies that held me shamefully down and prevented me from knowing and accepting the love and friendships of those around me. His lies forced me to build an impenetrable wall around myself and my heart. I would let no one near me, other than my husband and children.

Now, however, I am beginning to take down the wall. I am on a path for life. My secret loss will always be my loss, but thanks to God and his loving grace, the loss is one with which I can learn to live. The consequences of that choice remain forever, but I am forgiven. I am finally finding the life that I lost. Through him, I am able to have peace after abortion.

The path I am on is a path available for you as well. It is a path for everyone who seeks a relationship with God. It is a path for all who have made regrettable and seemingly unforgivable choices. It is a path for new life today and for all tomorrows.

*Trust in the Lord with all your heart*
*and lean not on your own understanding;*
*In all your ways acknowledge him,*
*and he will make your paths straight.*
Proverbs 3:5-6

Week 1

# What Is Wrong with Me?

*Cast all your anxiety on him because he cares for you.* 1 Peter 5:7

## Welcome & Purpose

Welcome to *My Secret Loss,* a small group study for women who have dealt either directly or indirectly with a crisis pregnancy that ended in abortion. The purpose of this study is to share the love, grace, and mercy of Christ Jesus between you and me (if you're reading this alone) or between you, your small group, and me (if you are participating in a small group study).

Through this workbook, I hope to share my story and bear your burdens. I sincerely express my love and encouragement to you, so you may find healing, hope, and joy.

## Opening Prayer

Dear God, our Father in heaven. We thank you for your loving and merciful presence with us this day. You know we come to you with our hearts burdened with feelings of regret, doubt, fear, guilt, confusion, and unworthiness. These are heavy loads, too much to carry by ourselves. We are here to bring these burdens to you, sharing them with each other and praying that you will remove them from our hearts. They make us weary, but we know you will give us strength, through your Son, Jesus Christ. In his name we pray. Amen.

*Come to me, all you who are weary and burdened, and I will give you rest. Take my yoke upon you and learn from me, for I am gentle and humble in heart, and you will find rest for your souls. For my yoke is easy and my burden is light.*
– Jesus, Matthew 11:28-30

## Meeting & Greeting

*If you are working through this workbook on your own, rather than participating in a small group study, please skip to the section entitled, "What Is Wrong With Me? A continuation of the author's story."*

This is *My Secret Loss* small group study. Each of us might be feeling a little uncomfortable or even nervous. But I'm certain those feelings will subside as soon as we get to know each other.

Please introduce yourselves. Tell us your name, a little about your family, and something special about yourself. Maybe you have a unique hobby, a special skill, or a particular love or passion for some aspect of life to share.

## Our Group Covenant

This study group is a covenant group. Covenants help us to build trust, share openly, and love and care for each other on the hills and in the valleys of our lives. A covenant group is based on love and a promise to treat everyone in the group with love. You know what love is. *Love is patient, love is kind. It does not envy, it does not boast, it is not proud. It is not rude, it is not self-seeking, it is not easily angered, and it keeps no record of wrongs. Love does not delight in evil but rejoices with the truth. It always protects, always trusts, always hopes, always perseveres* (1 Corinthians 13:4-8).

Some people are comfortable sharing their thoughts, feelings, concerns, worries, or fears within a group context. Somehow they live with a sense of love, trust, and freedom. But for many of us, it takes a while to build that feeling of confidence and trust with the others in the group. For some of us, someone in our past broke the trust we gave them, causing deep hurts.

Trust is needed before true sharing is possible. Trust is based on the knowledge that all group participants will respect one another, be honest, keep confidences, and not gossip or criticize. Trust is based on the knowledge that all group participants will treat each other with love.

Developing this trust can take months or even years of friendship within typical life circumstances. However, we need to begin building this sense of trust today, in order for our group to make the most of each weekly session.

To help resolve this issue, we need everyone's promise to be loving, trustworthy friends and sisters in Christ. Agreeing to a covenant for our group at the outset is important.

Please turn to the sample covenant in Appendix B. As a group, you can do with it as you wish: adopt it as it is, modify it to better suit the group, or use it as a sample and draft your own from scratch.

## Getting Started

When you signed up for this small group study, you were provided with this *My Secret Loss* workbook. As homework for the first session, you may have been asked to read the introductory materials, including the sections entitled "Introduction: Using this Workbook," "My Secret Loss: The Author's Story," and "Post-Abortion Stress: What is it?" If you did not read these things, you can do so before the next session. It is not critical that you have read such material before participating this week. However, you will find it useful to read it as soon as possible. These materials will help you understand the author and her situation and possibly help you find some common ground with her story.

For those who have read the introductory materials, was there anything in that material that either interested you or maybe surprised you? Why?

______________________________________________________________

______________________________________________________________

______________________________________________________________

## What Is Wrong with Me? A continuation of the author's story

*This section builds upon the author's initial story. For those participating in a small group study, volunteers are encouraged to read this piece aloud.*

It was my ten-year class reunion from high school. My husband was unable to go with me, so I attended alone. I was excited about going, secretly prepared to enjoy the anticipated positive attention as I noted what I was doing for a living, as I nonchalantly let on that I was doing well for myself, as I boasted about my two beautiful daughters and loving husband, and as I proved that I had my life under control. I wanted everyone to know I had succeeded in many of my high school dreams.

Upon seeing everyone at the reunion, I was surprised that I was feeling uncomfortable talking with my old friends. It wasn't at all like I had anticipated. I felt a need to latch on to a trusted friend and avoid mingling with the many others. I discovered I'd rather not say too much about myself, finding comfort in putting up an invisible wall between them and me.

During dinner, I enjoyed watching my old classmates getting up on stage, acting as the masters of ceremony and making presentations. I was impressed with their seemingly high levels of confidence and outgoing demeanors. I was glad I did not have to make the presentations.

After dinner when a girlfriend excused herself for a moment, I found myself standing alone. As I looked around to see who I might talk with next, my eyes landed on a young man who was part of the crowd that I often hung out with while in high school. At first I thought about talking to him, but suddenly without warning, my mood changed.

My mind slipped into the past as I watched him. I remembered that he had fathered a baby girl shortly after high school. The baby's mother was a friend of mine. After she discovered she was pregnant, she moved to another town to live with an older sister.

Standing motionless and staring at him, my thoughts dove deeper and deeper into my memory banks. *How could he do that to her? How could he get her pregnant and expect her to find a solution on her own?* I angrily accused him in my mind. *He abandoned her! He got her pregnant and just let her figure out what to do next.*

Now glaring at him with an unexpected hatred and rage, still standing motionless, I blamed him for making me deal with my pregnancy alone. I hated him for what he had done! He was despicable and his actions were unforgivable! Yes, I blamed and hated him for my high school pregnancy.

This man, who had no part in my own crisis pregnancy, suddenly and inexplicably became the symbol of the father of my aborted baby, the days of betrayal, the feelings of desperation, the fear of being alone and shunned by my friends and family, the reason for my choice, and the cause of my secret loss. This man, unexpectedly and at no fault of his own, became the object of my innumerable feelings of anger, hate, blame, shame, and rage.

As I glared at him with raw hatred, my thoughts returned to the present day, just as suddenly as they had slipped into the past. I saw that classmate looking at me with a look of confusion on his face. His eyes seemed to ask, *What? Me? What did I do? What's wrong?* Then his look changed, appearing to ask, *What's wrong with you?*

I shook my head as if just waking up from a dream. *Why did I do that? Why do I feel so angry and insecure? What's wrong with me?* I wondered to myself. *Forget about it. Pretend nothing ever happened. Don't tell anyone,* I directed myself.

## How Has Abortion Affected Me?

Review the following checklist. Which of these items have you observed in yourself (or in your friend or family member who had an abortion)?

- ☐ Do you feel anxious when you see pictures of an unborn baby?
- ☐ Do you try to compensate for past mistakes by working harder or trying to be more successful?
- ☐ Do you try to do everything perfectly, hoping to hide your past mistakes?
- ☐ Do you avoid trying new things because you do not know how to do them, being afraid that today's errors will showcase your past mistakes?
- ☐ Do you avoid places and events that might bring you in contact with acquaintances or friends you knew at the time of your abortion?
- ☐ Do you avoid locations that remind you of the abortion, such as the abortion clinic, the clinic's neighborhood, or the medical clinic in which your pregnancy was confirmed?
- ☐ Are you uncomfortable meeting new people and carrying on small talk?
- ☐ Do you avoid conversations that may involve heartfelt sharing of thoughts and feelings?
- ☐ Do you have a hard time forming close friendships, instead choosing to maintain a comfortable distance?
- ☐ Do you keep an invisible wall around yourself, exposing only that which is necessary for the immediate circumstances?
- ☐ Do you have trouble sleeping at night, thinking of the aborted baby or the abortion?
- ☐ Do you have difficulty forgiving yourself?

- ☐ Do you experience anxiety, anger, stress, or rage when abortion is mentioned in public, on television, or in conversation?
- ☐ Are your relationships strained with those who had a part in your decision to have an abortion?
- ☐ Do you repeatedly remind yourself to forget about the abortion or the baby?
- ☐ Do you obsessively desire to get pregnant again?
- ☐ Are you afraid to get pregnant again?
- ☐ Do you worry or believe something bad will happen to your children or someone you love as a punishment to you for having an abortion?
- ☐ Do you have dreams or flashbacks of your abortion?
- ☐ Do you feel anger or hate toward people involved in your abortion or in the decision to have an abortion?
- ☐ Do you feel anger or hate toward people you knew at the time of your unintended pregnancy?
- ☐ Do you find yourself frequently thinking about the baby, wondering what he or she would be like now?
- ☐ Do you have a sense of emptiness or hollow feeling like that which can come from a devastating loss?
- ☐ Are you emotionally numb, seemingly unable to develop feelings of love or attachment toward others?
- ☐ Are you afraid to develop a close bond with your children?
- ☐ Do you carry feelings of shame (feelings of self-hatred or dislike) based on your past choices?
- ☐ Do you continually and regularly grieve the loss of your baby, not diminishing with the passage of time?
- ☐ Do you become emotionally distraught (evidenced by sobbing, crying, weeping, or shuddering) when reminded of your abortion?

- ☐ Are you a workaholic, alcoholic, or drug user or abuser, possibly to escape memories of your abortion or thoughts of your lost baby?
- ☐ Are you a "pleaser," seeking to gain approval from all those around you?
- ☐ Do you have unrelenting feelings of sadness or bouts with depression?
- ☐ Do you have feelings of suicide?
- ☐ Do you fear God's judgment?
- ☐ Do you repeatedly ask God to forgive you for choosing abortion, fearing that he has not or will not forgive you?
- ☐ When talking or thinking about your abortion, do you become overwhelmed with feelings of guilt, shame, sorrow, or loss?
- ☐ If you don't have children, do you fear you will never be able to conceive a child?
- ☐ Has your self-esteem declined since the abortion, perhaps resulting in feelings of inferiority or unworthiness?
- ☐ Do you fear doctor's appointments or pelvic exams?
- ☐ Do you mistrust men or struggle in developing a healthy friendship, working relationship, or personal relationship with men?

Regardless of your answers to the above questions, know that God loves you. You are his daughter. He forgives you and he wants you to feel secure in his love.

If you severely struggle with low self-esteem, if you are unable to meet your daily responsibilities, if you suffer from depression, or if you struggle with thoughts of suicide, please seek professional help. Promptly contact your family physician, a Christian counselor, or a suicide prevention hotline. Help is available and I want you to reach out to those who can best serve your needs.

If you are not urgent and professional help is not needed, but you have checked five or more questions as applying to yourself (or your friend or family member), then I encourage you to continue working through this workbook. After finishing the workbook, you might conclude that you want even more materials or information.

In Appendix A you will find a number of recommended books and other resources you might want to consider. If you find only a few of the above-listed questions apply, you may still benefit from this workbook. Sometimes, as our understanding of a situation increases, we discover new information about ourselves that we had not noticed in the past.

## Why Am I Feeling This Way?

The author discovered a deep-seated, almost inexplicable and misplaced anger within her that surfaced when reminded of a friend's unplanned pregnancy.

With whom do you think she was really angry?

________________________________________

________________________________________

________________________________________

What do you think she was really angry about?

________________________________________

________________________________________

________________________________________

The author's feelings of anger were triggered by the memory of a friend's crisis pregnancy. What other events might trigger an onset of deep-felt but often hidden feelings?

________________________________________

________________________________________

________________________________________

What feelings about a past abortion have you (or your friend for family member) felt?

______________________________________________

______________________________________________

______________________________________________

How might such deep-seated feelings impact a post-abortive woman's life?

______________________________________________

______________________________________________

______________________________________________

Why do these feelings continually surface, being ever so hard to ignore?

______________________________________________

______________________________________________

______________________________________________

## Bible Study: David and Bathsheba

According to the book of Acts, David is described in God's words as a man after God's own heart (Acts 13:22). David was a great man, a man with qualities we all might like to have. You may recall that David was a loyal shepherd, a giant-slayer, the writer of many of the Psalms, a great king, and a person with a strong love for God. But David was not a perfect man. Like us, he made many poor choices in his life. He knowingly had a sexual relationship with a married woman and conceived a child with her. Then he abused his power as king to kill her husband, trying to hide the truth of his affair. Yet, he is described in the Bible as a man after God's heart. How could that be, we might wonder?

Let's read the story about David and Bathsheba. (Someone in the small group may volunteer to read aloud 2 Samuel 11:1-15.)

> *In the spring, at the time when kings go off to war, David sent Joab out with the king's men and the whole Israelite*

*army. They destroyed the Ammonites and besieged Rabbah. But David remained in Jerusalem.*

*One evening David got up from his bed and walked around on the roof of the palace. From the roof he saw a woman bathing. The woman was very beautiful, and David sent someone to find out about her. The man said, "Isn't this Bathsheba, the daughter of Eliam and the wife of Uriah the Hittite?" Then David sent messengers to get her. She came to him, and he slept with her. (She had purified herself from her uncleanness.) Then she went back home. The woman conceived and sent word to David, saying, "I am pregnant."*

*So David sent this word to Joab: "Send me Uriah the Hittite." And Joab sent him to David. When Uriah came to him, David asked him how Joab was, how the soldiers were and how the war was going. Then David said to Uriah, "Go down to your house and wash your feet." So Uriah left the palace, and a gift from the king was sent after him. But Uriah slept at the entrance to the palace with all his master's servants and did not go down to his house.*

*When David was told, "Uriah did not go home," he asked him, "Haven't you just come from a distance? Why didn't you go home?"*

*Uriah said to David, "The ark and Israel and Judah are staying in tents, and my master Joab and my lord's men are camped in the open fields. How could I go to my house to eat and drink and lie with my wife? As surely as you live, I will not do such a thing!"*

*Then David said to him, "Stay here one more day, and tomorrow I will send you back." So Uriah remained in Jerusalem that day and the next. At David's invitation, he ate and drank with him, and David made him drunk. But in the evening Uriah went out to sleep on his mat among his master's servants; he did not go home.*

> *In the morning David wrote a letter to Joab and sent it with Uriah. In it he wrote, "Put Uriah in the front line where the fighting is fiercest. Then withdraw from him so he will be struck down and die."*

When David discovered his act of adultery would be discovered through Bathsheba's pregnancy, what did he do to try to conceal it?

__________________________________________________________

__________________________________________________________

__________________________________________________________

In what ways might a choice to have an abortion be similar to David's actions?

__________________________________________________________

__________________________________________________________

__________________________________________________________

Facing God's punishment for his sins and laden with guilt and remorse, David wrote Psalm 51. Read aloud Psalm 51:1-3.

> *Have mercy on me, O God,*
> *according to your unfailing love;*
> *according to your great compassion*
> *blot out my transgressions.*
> *Wash away all my iniquity*
> *and cleanse me from my sin.*
> *For I know my transgressions,*
> *and my sin is always before me.*

What do you think David was feeling when he wrote Psalm 51?

__________________________________________________________

__________________________________________________________

__________________________________________________________

What can we learn in David's story about God's willingness to forgive our own regrettable choices of the past?

______________________________________________

______________________________________________

______________________________________________

Knowing he was forgiven, David wrote Psalm 32.
Read together Psalm 32:1-2.

> *Blessed is he*
> *whose transgressions are forgiven,*
> *whose sins are covered.*
> *Blessed is the man*
> *whose sin the Lord does not count against him*
> *and in whose spirit is no deceit.*

What does God's forgiveness do for us?

______________________________________________

______________________________________________

______________________________________________

David pleaded with God for forgiveness. He had committed adultery, tried to conceal it, and ultimately murdered the woman's husband. Yet, when David turned to God with a contrite heart, God forgave him. In exactly the same way, God forgives each of us. No sin is too great to be forgiven. Being forgiven and feeling forgiven are two separate things. When we seek forgiveness with a contrite heart, God forgives us whether or not we feel his forgiveness in our hearts. However, feeling God's forgiveness in our hearts can be an element of healing from our sense of shame.

Read Ecclesiastes 3:1-8.

*There is a time for everything,*

*and a season for every activity under heaven;*
*a time to be born and a time to die,*
*a time to plant and a time to uproot,*
*a time to kill and a time to heal,*
*a time to tear down and a time to build,*
*a time to weep and a time to laugh,*
*a time to mourn and a time to dance,*
*a time to scatter stones and a time to gather them,*
*a time to embrace and a time to refrain,*
*a time to search and a time to give up,*
*a time to keep and a time to throw away,*
*a time to tear and a time to mend,*
*a time to be silent and a time to speak,*
*a time to love and a time to hate,*
*a time for war and a time for peace.*

Is it time for you to search your heart, tear down and re-build, weep or mourn, keep your good memories, throw away the shame, and talk about it openly? Is it time for you to find love through Christ Jesus? Is it time for you to heal? Is it time to finally live the life God has planned for you? Yes, it is time. God loves you. His love gives each of us hope.

## Reflection & Encouragement

*There is no medicine like hope, no incentive so great, and no tonic so powerful as expectation of something better tomorrow.* – Orison Swett Marden[4]

## Memory Verse

*Why are you downcast, O my soul?*
*Why so disturbed within me?*

4 Orison Swett Marden, "Orison Swett Marden Quotes," 2001-2015, Brainy Quote, 14 January 2015, http://www.brainyquote.com/quotes/authors/o/orison_swett_marden.html

*Put your hope in God,*
*for I will yet praise him,*
*my Savior and my God.*
Psalm 42:5

## Closing Prayer

Dear Lord, we are so grateful for your steadfast love and never-ending mercy. We ask you to come near to us and hold our hearts in your loving hands as we begin to travel down this path and dig into the mistakes of our pasts. Enable us to open our hearts and our minds to a greater understanding of our past choices and how those choices have impacted our lives, our relationships, and the lives of many others. Then, through your mercy and grace, help us to know and accept your forgiveness and healing touch. Bring us peace. In you, we place our hope. In Jesus' name we pray. Amen.

## Homework

- If you have not already done so, read the sections entitled, "Introduction: Using this Workbook," "My Secret Loss: The Author's Story," and "Post-Abortion Stress: What is it?"
- If you are participating in a small group study, read through Week 2 of the workbook to prepare for next week's group.
- Place copies of the memory verse in convenient locations in your home and place of employment (such as on your bathroom mirror, by the kitchen sink, on the dash of your car, or on your office desk). Read it several times each day until you have committed it to memory. A page containing multiple copies of the memory verse is provided in Appendix C for you to use for this purpose.
- At home, at a quiet time, prayerfully (asking God to guide

your thoughts) think through the following questions. You will find it helpful to write your answers in a journal.

1. Describe the feelings you have today about the fact that you had an abortion.

2. Describe how you felt on the day of your abortion. (Maybe you felt fear, relief, anger, sorrow, nervousness, confusion, guilt, or sadness.)

3. Do you believe that your abortion has impacted your relationships with others? In what ways?

4. Where were you in your faith journey with God at the time of your abortion? Has the abortion impacted your relationship with God? How?

Week 2

# But It Was Legal!

*Let us draw near to God with a sincere heart in full assurance of faith, having our hearts sprinkled to cleanse us from a guilty conscience and having our bodies washed with pure water.* Hebrews 10:22

## Opening Prayer

Dear Holy Father, your strength has carried us to this point, a point that can be frightening to us. As we dig deeper into a period of discovery regarding our past choices, we often find ourselves fearful of our feelings and the reactions of others in our lives. We thank you for supportive friends, small group members, the author of this workbook, and all others who compassionately empathize with our thoughts, concerns and fears. It often seems easier to deny the truth, deny the paths we have taken, and deny you. Forgive us. We thank you for your constant support, your never-ending love, and your gifts of grace. Amen.

## Meeting & Greeting

*If you are working through this workbook on your own rather than participating in a small group study, please skip to the section entitled, "Getting Started."*

Welcome to the second week in the *My Secret Loss* small group study.

We are very happy that you are all here today. To open the conversation, let's go around the room and introduce ourselves again.

This week, tell us about an embarrassing moment in your life, either as a child, teenager, or even very recently.

## Getting Started

What feelings do you think are most common for women at the time they decide to have an abortion?

______________________________

______________________________

______________________________

What feelings do you think are most common to women immediately after having the abortion? Do you think these feelings change over time?

______________________________

______________________________

______________________________

## But It Was Legal! A continuation of the author's story

*Again, this section builds upon the author's initial story. If you are participating in a small group study, please ask for a volunteer to read this piece aloud.*

I occasionally get surprised by the descriptions some people use for an aborted baby. Recently, I was watching an interview on television with a doctor whose practice is to perform abortions. He called the aborted babies "specimens." Maybe that term makes it easier for him to do what he does as a profession. Maybe by calling them specimens, this doctor is able to guard his heart. Maybe it enables him to avoid guilt, shame, or remorse.

When I had my abortion, I was told the baby was just tissue. I was told my body was building a "nest" for the baby; it wasn't a baby yet. I believed what I was told. I believed the baby didn't really exist yet. For many years, I wanted to believe the baby was just tissue, a type of "nest." Even as time went on and I became better informed, I tried to convince myself that I aborted tissue and simply managed a health condition.

I wanted the baby to be just tissue. I needed the baby to be just tissue. I never thought of the word "specimen," but I might have found comfort in that term too, at least for a while.

I recall talking to my sister one day. She didn't yet know about my high school pregnancy and abortion. There had been something on the news about an abortion clinic. If I remember correctly, it had to do with someone radically trying to change our country's stance on abortion by bombing the clinic.

In our conversation, I tried to carefully, without disclosing my past choice, emphasize that abortion is legal and it should stay legal. At the time, I still did not believe abortion was taking the life of a pre-born infant. I gave my sister all of the reasons for my opinion: some girls are desperate and have nowhere to turn; some girls will resort to attempted suicide; some women have been raped; it should be a woman's right to decide when to have a child and when not to have a child; and we can't allow the system to return to the unsafe, illegal conditions of the past. My arguments went on and on.

She wasn't convinced. I wanted so badly to believe my arguments. However, deep down I was only partially convinced. Something was tugging at my heart.

After our daughters were born and I fully understood that a baby begins to form upon conception, my arguments focused on an idea that a baby in the womb is just a body forming. It is not yet a baby or a person with feelings or personality. "The baby is not a baby until it is born alive," I would argue to my sister.

My sister still wasn't convinced, and I was only partially convinced. I still wanted very badly to believe my arguments. However, something kept tugging at my heart.

Yet in later arguments, I resorted to the idea that the baby doesn't have a soul until it is born. My sister's silent response told me that my theory was still not correct.

*But it doesn't matter what my sister believes*, I'd argue to myself. *My choice was legal. I did nothing wrong in the eyes of the law, in the eyes of our government, and in the eyes of many people. It was legal. So, it can't be wrong.*

Is it wrong even when it is legal?

As the years passed with this nagging question weighing on my heart, I eventually found myself wondering what the baby would have looked like, what he would have liked and disliked, and what our lives together could have been if I had not had the abortion.

*Don't even think about it*, I'd tell myself. *It is over. It was long ago. It was legal.* Deep in my heart, the truth remained and it tried to surface for many years. However, it seemed easier to deny the baby's existence. How could I face myself and others if I admitted or accepted that the aborted tissue was a real, living baby? How could I accept this as truth and yet live with my decision, live with the guilt, live with the shame? I couldn't accept it as truth. I wouldn't accept it as truth, not for many years.

In time, however, I began to listen to my heart. I now know what was tugging at it for so many years. At some point I made a new choice. I accepted as fact that the tissue I aborted was a baby, a baby growing as any baby would grow. It was no less a baby just because it was smaller. Today, I face this truth, but I have also found freedom in this truth.

Denial is a sign of guilt. No longer denying the truth, I have been able to recognize my feelings of guilt. Satan has used my healthy feelings of guilt, feelings I have tried to suppress for many years, to give me shame. Satan's shame has been a weight on my shoulders, at times nearly breaking my spirit. Satan's shame has held me down and encompassed me like a prison. It has prevented me from finding God's grace and mercy for my life. Ending the denial has given me the freedom to feel healthy guilt and the ability to shed Satan's shame through the grace and mercy of Jesus Christ.

*I will give you a new heart and put a new spirit in you; I will remove from you your heart of stone and give you a heart of flesh.* Ezekiel 36:26

### Denial, God's Guilt, Satan's Shame

In the same way a child will tell his mother, "I didn't do it," many women will deny their abortion through means of justification. *It wasn't a baby yet. I didn't have correct information. I had no other choice. Everyone said it was the best thing to do.*

What purpose does denial serve?

______________________________

______________________________

______________________________

Why do you think many people try to avoid thinking that abortion terminates a life?

______________________________

______________________________

______________________________

What ways might a woman use to deny the reality of her decision to have an abortion?

______________________________

______________________________

______________________________

How can denial hinder or interfere with the process of healing after the abortion?

______________________________

______________________________

What is guilt? Why would the author believe that guilt is a healthy feeling?

The author states that denial is a sign of guilt. In what other ways might feelings of guilt manifest themselves?

Why would a woman feel guilty about choosing abortion if the abortion was legal?

Shame is a state of disgrace or a feeling of dishonor. It is a "painful emotion caused by consciousness of guilt, shortcoming, or impropriety."[5] How does shame differ from guilt?

> *The thief comes only to steal and kill and destroy; I have come that they may have life, and have it to the full.* – Jesus, John 10:10

Shame is a tool of Satan. By using our guilt against us, he constantly badgers us. Through his badgering, we begin to believe that we should be alone, we are not worthy of friendship or love, and everyone who

5 *Merriam-Webster's Collegiate Dictionary*, 11th ed., 2004, s.v. "shame."

learns of our abortion will condemn us. He wants to rob us of our relationships with God, our families, and all those who matter most to us. He uses shame to destroy us.

Through Jesus we can shed the feelings of shame. Once we know we will not face shame, we can start to break down the walls built through our forms of denial and begin to face our feelings of guilt. Feelings of guilt create a humble heart, a heart that seeks and receives forgiveness from our Lord, Jesus.

Let go of Satan's shame. It does not belong to you. God does not intend for you to live in shame. Now, let go of denial. Only then can we face our feelings of guilt, grief, and anger head on, knowing the strength of our Lord is with us.

> *I sought the Lord, and he answered me;*
> *he delivered me from all my fears.*
> *Those who look to him are radiant;*
> *their faces are never covered with shame.*
> Psalm 34:4-5

## What Is the Truth about Abortion?

Randy Alcorn's book *Why Pro-Life?* provides a scientific and practical description on why we can know for certain that life begins at conception. (His book is listed in Appendix A as recommended reading.) We are often inundated with pro-life promotional pictures depicting a developing fetus. Many of us have had children of our own and have seen the ultrasound pictures of the baby as it develops. Some of us may have seen the famous photo of the twenty-one-week-old, pre-born infant holding the finger of a surgeon outside of the mother's womb as surgery is performed to resolve a birth defect. The scientific evidence is conclusive that immediately following conception, living cells begin to divide and a baby begins to take shape.

In my denial, I tried to argue with my sister that it was true the baby is beginning to take shape, but it still wasn't a baby. The logic of that argument fails when you ask yourself, "Is a newborn less human than a child?" The clear answer is no, the newborn is simply less developed than a child. So, the question to consider becomes, "Is a pre-born baby less human than a newborn?" The answer is again no. The pre-born baby is simply less developed than the newborn. Finally, "Is the newly conceived baby less human than a pre-born baby who is eight months old since conception?" Isn't the newly conceived baby simply less developed? It is still human.

Also in my various stages of denial, I argued with my sister that the baby doesn't have a personality until it is born. Therefore, it is not really a person. It seems that this claim can be refuted in much the same way as the first. Consider what kind of personality a newborn has as compared to an adult. The personality is simply less developed. Does that make the newborn less human? No. The same would hold true for the pre-born or newly conceived baby.

Finally, I boldly and desperately clung to the argument that the baby, while alive in the womb, does not have significance because it has no soul. I wanted to believe that the baby has no soul until birth. In my theory, the soul would enter the baby's body miraculously with the baby's first breath. This made sense to me, especially when I considered that the soul left the body with a person's last breath of life. I held tight to that argument for several years. It was the only argument I had left. Without it, I had only my guilt and shame.

## Bible Study

Please read Psalm 139:13-16.

> *For you created my inmost being;*
> *you knit me together in my mother's womb.*
> *I praise you because I am fearfully and wonderfully made;*
> *your works are wonderful,*
> *I know that full well.*
> *My frame was not hidden from you*
> *when I was made in the secret place.*

*When I was woven together in the depths of the earth,*
*your eyes saw my unformed body.*
*All the days ordained for me*
*were written in your book*
*before one of them came to be.*

What does Psalm 139:13-16 say about the formation of life?

______________________________________________

______________________________________________

______________________________________________

God has a plan for each of us. Again looking at Psalm 139, particularly the last sentence quoted above, when does he make this plan for us?

______________________________________________

______________________________________________

______________________________________________

Read Matthew 18:10.

*See that you do not look down on one of these little ones. For I tell you that their angels in heaven always see the face of my Father in heaven.*

Read Isaiah 46:3.

*Listen to me, O house of Jacob, all you who remain of the house of Israel, you whom I have upheld since you were conceived, and have carried since your birth.*

From Matthew, we know that God takes special care of our children, because Jesus tells us there are angels in heaven for each of our children and these angels always see the face of God. Looking at the verse from Isaiah, when does God begin caring for our children?

The story of Mary and Elizabeth gives incredible insight to the beginning of life. This story begins just after the angel visits Mary, a virgin, and tells her she has found favor with God, will be pregnant, and give birth to a son who would be called the Son of the Most High. At this same time, Mary's relative, Elizabeth, who was older and barren, is now six months pregnant. Please read Luke 1:39-45 and 56 to hear what happens next.

> *At that time Mary got ready and hurried to a town in the hill country of Judea, where she entered Zechariah's home and greeted Elizabeth. When Elizabeth heard Mary's greeting, the baby leaped in her womb, and Elizabeth was filled with the Holy Spirit. In a loud voice she exclaimed: "Blessed are you among women, and blessed is the child you will bear! But why am I so favored, that the mother of my Lord should come to me? As soon as the sound of your greeting reached my ears, the baby in my womb leaped for joy. Blessed is she who has believed that what the Lord has said to her will be accomplished!" ...*
>
> *Mary stayed with Elizabeth for about three months and then returned home.*

Elizabeth's baby, only six months old since conception, leaped for joy in Elizabeth's womb at the sound of Mary's voice. What does that tell us about a pre-born baby's life and soul?

________________________________________

________________________________________

________________________________________

At the time of this story, Mary was just days pregnant. Elizabeth, who was filled with the Holy Spirit giving her knowledge of Mary's pregnancy, called Mary's baby "Lord." What do Elizabeth's words tell us about the life and soul of a newly conceived baby?

________________________________________

________________________________________

________________________________________

If we accept that the pre-born baby was a person for whom God had a plan at the time of the abortion, what are some things we can do to relieve ourselves from our feelings of guilt or shame that might naturally surface?

______________________________________________

______________________________________________

______________________________________________

## Reflection & Encouragement

In 1999, Dr. Tony Evans shared the experience of a seasoned chess champion touring an art museum. While passing through the gallery, his attention was drawn to a painting that involved chess. The artist had painted a match between Satan and an outwitted young man. The picture frozen on canvas showed the two engaged in a chess game being played out for the man's soul. The man was in obvious panic as the adversary's hand was making his final move. The artist's work is simply titled *Checkmate*. The chess champion stood and observed the painting for a long time. His scowl of concentration was finally softened by a slight smile. He turned to the curator and said, "I've got good news for the man in that picture. He still has a move." The father of lies has convinced too many people that he has placed them in checkmate, but the grace of God has provided every man with the hope that "he still has a move."[6]

## Memory Verse

> *The Lord is close to the brokenhearted*
> *and saves those who are crushed in spirit.*
> Psalm 34:18

6 Tony Evans, "Passion of the Gospel," 1999, as quoted in Raymond McHenry, *McHenry's Stories for the Soul* (Peabody MA: Hendrickson Publishers, 2001), 146.

## Closing Prayer

Father God, your strength lifts us and carries us through all times of trouble. As we let down our defenses and face the truth about our past choices, our hearts may break, but we know that you are forever close. As we work through our healthy feelings of guilt, protect us from Satan's lies. We ask for your strength to fight his shame that stands to crush our spirits. Do not let him steal or destroy the purpose and joy you have planned for our lives. We know that at all times, no matter what we have done or left undone, you will always provide a path leading to you, through your Son, Jesus Christ. We thank you for your gift of forgiveness and salvation. Amen.

## Homework

Place copies of the memory verse in convenient locations in your home and place of employment. Read it several times each day until you have committed it to memory.

If you are participating in a small group study, read through Week 3 of the workbook to prepare for next week's group.

Write a list stating all of the factors that impacted your decision (or the decision of your friend or family member) to have an abortion.

- What pressures were you facing?
- What did you feel anxious about?
- What fears did you have?
- What did you tell yourself to justify your decision?
- What did you tell yourself to deny your loss?
- How has trying to deny your abortion impacted your life (your relationships, your personality, and your esteem)?

## Week 3

# I Ran and Hid, But I Could Not Escape

*If we claim to be without sin, we deceive ourselves and the truth is not in us. If we confess our sins, he is faithful and just and will forgive us our sins and purify us from all unrighteousness. If we claim we have not sinned, we make him out to be a liar and his word has no place in our lives.* 1 John 1:8-10

### Opening Prayer

Father God, we ask you to join us today as we continue on this path of discovery. Your love encourages us to seek the truth, and your strength upholds us as we discover the truth. We thank you for your steadfast love and mercy and constant support. We know we have done wrong in your eyes in many ways. We know we sometimes do not recognize our sins. We are humbled by our sinfulness. Forgive us Lord. We pray this in the name of Jesus Christ. Amen.

### Meeting & Greeting

*If you are working through this workbook on your own rather than participating in a small group study, please skip to the section entitled, "I Ran and Hid, but I Could Not Escape! A continuation of the author's story."*

Welcome to our third week in the *My Secret Loss* small group study. As always, we are very happy you are all here today.

This week share with us what, when you were a child, you wanted to be when you grew up.

______________________________________________

______________________________________________

______________________________________________

## Getting Started

When doing your homework, did you discover anything about the impact of your abortion or the denial of it on your relationships, your personality, or your self-esteem that you would like to share with the group?

______________________________________________

______________________________________________

______________________________________________

## I Ran and Hid, but I Could Not Escape! A continuation of the author's story

*Again, this section builds upon the author's initial story. Volunteers from the small group are encouraged to read this piece aloud.*

After the abortion, I resolved to start over.

*I'll put everything behind me. I'll make sure no one knows of my choices. And above all, I will be the best person I can possibly be. That way, no one will ever need to know of the choices I have made.* So began my quest for respect, assurance of value, and freedom from the memories and resultant feelings created by my regrettable choices.

Throughout the following years, I lived my new life. I graduated from high school in January, a semester early. I finished college in three-and-a-half years. I got a good job as an engineer with a major computer company. I tried to do everything that was expected of me.

I was living within expectations, but I wasn't satisfied. I needed something more. I didn't understand my problem exactly, so I concluded I had to do more with my life. I concluded I needed to expand my career options.

After three years working as an engineer, I left my job and went on to law school. There I met Wayne. He was my knight-in-shining-armor, my prince charming. We got married while I was still in law school. What a comfortable, loving feeling. I was married. He loved me. I was part of a couple, a twosome, and a marital partnership. I was living a respectable life and it felt good.

Even with all these good things in my life, I still felt driven to gain more approval from others. It seemed like I needed constant reassurances that I was doing the right thing. I thrived on positive feedback, working harder and harder to gain the next positive fix. However, each positive fix lasted only a short while until something rather unidentifiable would again weigh heavily on my heart.

I found myself fretting over whether I said the right thing or whether I had the right clothing or whether I'd be liked. My sense of worth seemed to depend on the opinions of others. I needed to know they (whoever "they" might have been) approved of me or of what I was doing. I needed their signs of approval. Such signs told me I wasn't a bad person; I was ok. Their signs of approval helped me to believe I was and could be a respectable and likeable person.

Upon graduation from law school, I found a great job with a major corporation. I worked hard to do well, thriving again on all signs of approval, such as job promotions, pay increases, and respect from my colleagues. I loved the regular assurances that I was a valued employee. I had value.

Or did I? Again, something kept telling my heart I wasn't quite good enough.

I had good friends, a husband, and a good job. I was living the American dream; but what was wrong? I still felt something wasn't right. I wasn't content. True contentedness seemed to evade me. I continued to feel like I had to be careful. *Watch what you say*, I'd tell myself. *Don't do anything wrong. Be sure you are dressed right. Always be careful about what you say or do. Above all, hide your past choices and do not tell anyone of your secret loss.* Whether I recognized it or not, nothing could eliminate the deep down consequences from my heart that had resulted from my abortion.

> *You are my hiding place;*
> *you will protect me from trouble*
> *and surround me with songs of deliverance.*
> Psalm 32:7

For many years, I carefully hid my abortion from everyone. My husband Wayne was the only one I confided in. I told him about it shortly after he asked me to marry him. I was so afraid he would no longer want to marry me. I thought for sure I'd lose him; but I also believed we could not start our marriage with my past choices held in secret. When I finally got up the courage to say the words, I couldn't look at him. I could only look away. I told him I would understand if he no longer wanted to marry me. Then I saw a glimpse of what true love was all about. Wayne showed me compassion. He still loved me.

It was good to have finally told someone. A burden was lifted. I thought I could finally put my regrettable choices behind me. I wanted to believe the abortion no longer mattered. I wanted to forget about it. I wanted to move on with my life. But it didn't work that way. I could never forget. Reminders were everywhere.

At doctors' offices, the registration forms often asked, "How many pregnancies have you had?" I always struggled with the answer. I decided I'd tell them only if they really needed to know. I was there for a headache. They didn't need to know. I was there for an annual checkup. They didn't need to know. I was there for an illness. They didn't need to know. I was there because I was pregnant. Maybe they needed to know. No, on second thought, they didn't need to know. *Hide it*, I thought as I lied on the forms.

Then, there were the times abortion came up as the topic of

conversation with friends or family members. Usually something in the news would cause someone to start the conversation. "It should be against the law," someone would say. "It's wrong! How can anyone even think about killing their baby like that?" another would add with greater intensity and disgust.

*Hide it*, I'd remind myself. *They will never understand.* I had no options but to hide my choices, hide my guilt, and hide my shame. I had to live with my past choices in silence. There was no escape.

Then came the time when our daughters came home from their church youth group armed with pro-life, anti-abortion materials. They asked rhetorically and with a tone of disgust, "How could anyone do that? How could a woman be so cold?"

My heart sank. *Hide it*, I cried to myself.

No matter how hard I tried to hide it, my choice would not go away. It was part of my regrettable past, and I could not escape my feelings of guilt. Yet I could not tell anyone. The things I feared most, loss of the love of family or friends, made it too risky to tell anyone. Nothing I did removed the guilt. Nothing I did enabled me to forget my choices. My choices and their consequences never went away.

I ran and I hid, but I couldn't escape.

> *He who conceals his sins does not prosper,*
> *but whoever confesses and renounces them finds mercy.*
> Proverbs 28:13

## The Many Ways to Hide

The author thought she could start life over and hide her abortion from others by doing her best at all she pursued. What other things might a woman do to hide from others the fact that she had an abortion?

________________________________________

________________________________________

________________________________________

Why would a woman believe she needs to hide her abortion from other people?

> *Therefore, there is now no condemnation for those who are in Christ Jesus, because through Christ Jesus the law of the Spirit of life set me free from the law of sin and death.*
> Romans 8:1-2

The author was also trying to forget the memories of her abortion and put them far into the past. Why is there often a strong attempt to escape the memories of one's abortion?

List the many things a woman might do in order to forget about her abortion.

The author noted a sense of relief when she told her fiancé about her abortion. Why does talking about our mistakes make us feel better?

To whom can we safely talk about our abortion and the mistakes we made?

___

___

___

*Nothing in all creation is hidden from God's sight. Everything is uncovered and laid bare before the eyes of him to whom we must give account.* Hebrews 4:13

## Bible Study

You are probably familiar with the story about Adam and Eve. After Eve gave in to the serpent's temptations and ate of the forbidden fruit, she gave some to Adam and he ate it too. So they both chose to act directly contrary to God's command. For today's discussion, read what happens next. Please read Genesis 3:8-13.

*Then the man and his wife heard the sound of the Lord God as he was walking in the garden in the cool of the day, and they hid from the Lord God among the trees of the garden. But the Lord God called to the man, "Where are you?"*

*He answered, "I heard you in the garden, and I was afraid because I was naked; so I hid."*

*And he said, "Who told you that you were naked? Have you eaten from the tree that I commanded you not to eat from?"*

*The man said, "The woman you put here with me – she gave me some fruit from the tree, and I ate it."*

*Then the Lord God said to the woman, "What is this you have done?"*

*The woman said, "The serpent deceived me, and I ate."*

Adam and Eve disobeyed God. In what ways did they try to hide their sin from God?

________________________________________

________________________________________

________________________________________

Do you think God knew about their sin before he talked with Adam and Eve in the garden? Explain.

________________________________________

________________________________________

________________________________________

Some of us may have successfully hidden our abortion from family members or our friends. Do you believe we can hide this choice from God? Discuss why or why not.

________________________________________

________________________________________

________________________________________

Adam and Eve initially had two children who are mentioned in the Bible, Cain and Abel. Abel was a shepherd and Cain was a crop farmer. Each of them brought gifts to God; Abel brought the fat portions from some of the firstborn of his flock. In contrast, Cain brought some of the fruits of the soil as an offering. God looked at Abel with favor, which made Cain very angry. So, out of jealousy, Cain killed Abel. Let's read what happens next in Genesis 4:9-15.

> *Then the Lord said to Cain, "Where is your brother Abel?"*
>
> *"I don't know," he replied. "Am I my brother's keeper?"*
>
> *The Lord said, "What have you done? Listen! Your brother's blood cries out to me from the ground. Now you are under a curse and driven from the ground, which opened its mouth*

*to receive your brother's blood from your hand. When you work the ground, it will no longer yield its crops for you. You will be a restless wanderer on the earth."*

*Cain said to the Lord, "My punishment is more than I can bear. Today you are driving me from the land, and I will be hidden from your presence; I will be a restless wanderer on the earth, and whoever finds me will kill me."*

*But the Lord said to him, "Not so, if anyone kills Cain, he will suffer vengeance seven times over." Then the Lord put a mark on Cain so that no one who found him would kill him.*

Cain tried to hide his sin from God by claiming he didn't know what happened to his brother; but God knew what Cain had done. Do you think we can hide any of our sins from God?

______________________________________________

______________________________________________

______________________________________________

Cain faced lifelong consequences for murdering his brother. What lifelong consequences do you feel you (or your friend or family member) face as a result of abortion?

______________________________________________

______________________________________________

______________________________________________

What lifelong consequences do you believe are faced by others who may be involved in a woman's abortion (i.e., the doctor, the woman's parents, and the boyfriend or husband)?

______________________________________________

______________________________________________

______________________________________________

Even though God punished Cain for his sin, how did God show that he still loved Cain?

---

---

---

Please read Psalm 32:3-5.

*When I kept silent,*
*my bones wasted away*
*through my groaning all day long*
*For day and night*
*your hand was heavy upon me;*
*my strength was sapped as in the heat of summer.*
*Then I acknowledged my sin to you*
*and did not cover up my iniquity.*
*I said, "I will confess*
*my transgressions to the Lord" –*
*and you forgave*
*the guilt of my sin.*

David wrote this Psalm as a result of his affair with Bathsheba. He said, For day and night your hand was heavy upon me? Describe how it might feel to have God's hand heavy upon you.

---

---

---

To lift God's heavy hand, David confessed his sin. Why would confessing our sins have a healing impact?

---

---

---

For those participating in a small group, break into pairs and confess to your partner your decision to have an abortion. If you are here to help or understand a family member or friend or if you do not feel ready to confess your abortion at this time, confess another sin that has been weighing on your heart. Together pray for God's forgiveness for both of you. (If you are working privately through this workbook and you do not feel you have a safe person to whom you can confess, consider making an appointment with your church pastor and confess to him or her. Alternatively, feel free to send an e-mail of confession to the author, sl@connectingchoices.com, or write your confession in a letter to God.)

> *If we confess our sins, he is faithful and just and will forgive us our sins and purify us from all unrighteousness.*
> 1 John 1:9

## Reflection & Encouragement

Hide, little girl, beneath your Mama's skirt
Hide, little girl, and maybe it won't hurt
Hide from the laughter, what if it's at you?
Hide from the sorrow so no one has a clue.
Hide, little girl, behind the smile you learned
Hide beneath the masquerade of credits that you earned
Hide in crowded corridors until the school day ends
Hide in courts of favor but never trust a friend.
Hide, little girl, behind your wedding veil
Eyes that cannot cry are eyes that tattletale.
Hide, little girl, until your time runs out
Can't always hide, little girl, one day you'll be found out.
You can run, little girl, to the only One who knows
To a place of fertile soil where trust can finally grow
Then you can hide, little girl, 'til every eye may see
You found, little girl, safely hid in Me.

– Beth Moore[7]

7 Used by permission from Beth Moore, *Things Pondered* (Nashville: B&H Publishing Group, 2004), 73.

## Memory Verse

*If we confess our sins, he is faithful and just and will forgive us our sins and purify us from all unrighteousness.*
1 John 1:9

## Closing Prayer

Dear Father in heaven; thank you for this opportunity to build our relationship with you. We know we cannot run from our transgressions because nothing is hidden from your sight. We fear disclosure to others. We fear their reaction. We do not want to face their condemnation. Now, however, we know you are our place of refuge. Through your love and forgiveness, we are protected. Your love is our hiding place. Thank you, dear Father. Amen.

## Homework

- Place copies of the memory verse in convenient locations in your home and place of employment. Read it several times each day until you have committed it to memory.
- If you are participating in a small group study, read through Week 4 of the workbook to prepare for next week's group study.
- List the various things you have done in an attempt to run from or hide your abortion and related choices from your own heart and from other people.
- List the key people in your life from whom you have hidden your abortion and note why you have kept this secret from them. Write a letter of confession to each of these people in your journal. (Please note: This is intended to

be a personal exercise. The letters should be kept in your journal and not mailed.)

- Pray. Ask God to deliver your confessions in his own way and in his own time to those who have been affected by your abortion(s).
- In what ways do you believe God has disciplined you for your past mistakes? How have you grown from his discipline?

## Week 4

# Mourning My Secret Loss

*A voice is heard in Ramah, mourning and great weeping, Rachel weeping for her children and refusing to be comforted, because her children are no more.* Jeremiah 31:15

### Opening Prayer

Dear Father in heaven; you have faithfully shown us your love each week, enabling us to go on. As we explore our complicated and conflicting feelings of denial, anger, and sorrow, we ask you to lead us to acceptance, acceptance of your loving grace and forgiveness, acceptance of your healing touch. Be constantly with us, dear Lord. In Jesus' glorious name we pray. Amen.

### Meeting & Greeting

*If you are working through this workbook on your own rather than participating in a small group study, please skip to the section entitled, "Getting Started."*

Welcome to our fourth week in the *My Secret Loss* small group study. Thank you for continuing to support each other as we walk through the author's stories and relate them to ourselves, our family members, or our friends.

This week, please tell us about your favorite pet, which you have now, have had in your past, or have always wanted to have.

___

___

___

## Getting Started

Thinking of all the people from whom we have deliberately kept our abortions a secret, discuss reasons why it would be wise to share our secret losses and reasons why it would be wise to continue keeping our losses quiet.

___

___

___

What can we do to help us discern when the time is right for us to tell those closest to us about our abortions?

___

___

___

## Mourning My Secret Loss: A continuation of the author's story

*As before, this section builds upon the author's initial story. Volunteers from the small group study are invited to read this piece aloud.*

It was early in the morning on December 26th. I was just nine years old and had awakened from a wonderful night's rest, dreaming with joy following a very happy Christmas. I could hear my mother talking to someone. *Why is she home?* I wondered. *Maybe they let Daddy out of the hospital. He looked kind of good when we saw him yesterday. He smiled!* I was so glad the hospital let us see him on Christmas day, even if it was for only five minutes each.

He was in a special section of the hospital. They normally didn't allow visitors, just Mom. Mom said he had a blood clot in his heart, but it was getting better.

I looked out the window and saw a car that I didn't recognize. I hurried downstairs to see what was going on.

Everyone was sitting at the kitchen table. Grandpa, Grandma, Mom, and our pastor were there. The other kids weren't out of bed yet, so I was the only young one in the room.

Grandma said, "Sit down, Sheila. We have something to tell you."

Just then the phone rang, and my mother went to the dining room to answer. While Mom was on the phone, Grandma said cautiously, "Sheila, your daddy went to be with Kandyce."

*What?* I wondered to myself. I didn't know what she meant. I didn't know where Kandyce was. She was my oldest sister. She left our home before I was three years old. She had been very sick, I knew. It was cancer, they later told me. Then she died. But where did she go? And, how could Daddy go there too?

Then my brothers and my sister came downstairs and joined the group. After they all sat down, Grandma said, "Your daddy died last night. He's gone to heaven."

Catching my breath, I now understood. Kandyce died and then she went to heaven. Daddy died and now he went to heaven. Heaven must be very far away. When people go there, they never come back.

Daddy will never come back.

The thought sickened me. I felt like I needed to throw up. I ran up to my bedroom to be alone. I opened the window to let the cold winter air relieve the sick feeling in my stomach by cooling my face and my neck. Then I sobbed. I knew he'd never come back.

I touched the frost that had formed on the glass and watched it disappear.

Daddy was gone.

I missed Daddy then and forevermore. I wanted to sit on his lap again. I wanted him to sing that song he would sing to me, "You are my sunshine . . ." I wanted him to tuck me in bed at night. I wanted him to teach me how to dance. I wanted him to tell me he was proud of me. I wanted him to love me.

The reminders of his untimely death never go away. When I think time has healed the wound, something happens again to remind me: high school graduation, college graduation, the excitement of my first job, my wedding as I wished he could walk with me down the aisle, law school graduation, the birth of our daughters without this grandfather to welcome them with love, and always and forever Christmas, the anniversary of his death. It's been almost fifty years since he died.

The loss of a pre-born baby is a wound that stays with you for a lifetime, too. Ask women who have had miscarriages. Many will tell you they grieve for their lost child. They also find that not everyone understands their grief. Many people in our society do not understand that God blesses us with love for our unborn children. So losing a child before birth can be just as painful as losing an infant after birth. One difference lies in the limited means in our society to mourn the loss of our pre-born babies.

I've learned how to grieve and live with the losses of my father and other family members, but how do I grieve a loss created by my own actions? Can I mourn the loss of a baby when I chose to end the pregnancy? Is it okay to feel grief in this case?

I remember as a little girl always wanting a younger brother or sister. I wished and wished and wished for this new sibling. When I learned that a new brother or sister was not possible, I began to dream about the day I would be pregnant. Oh, how I wanted a baby to love and take care of. The dreams of a little girl are often filled with plans for babies of her own.

Not many years later, I became pregnant. The reality wasn't the same as my childhood dreams. The reality came with thoughts and fears of practical responsibility, coupled with public shame and the belief that I'd lose all the family and friends I knew. Which loss would be greater, the unknown or the perceived known? All choices at that point in my life created a loss for me. So I chose the loss I thought would be the easiest to bear. Thereafter, through the strength of my will and convictions, I denied the loss.

Only recently have I allowed the discovery of the true loss to surface. Losing a pre-born baby includes the loss of hopes and dreams for his or her future, the loss of a loving mother and child relationship, and the loss of one of God's intended blessings, whether the blessing was intended for me or for an adoptive family. The loss is far-reaching, impacting my life, impacting my family today, and impacting the lives of countless unknown people. It doesn't matter how the loss came about.

Yes, we may grieve the loss of our pre-born babies regardless of the circumstances of their deaths. As with my father, constant reminders of my baby's life who never came to be surround me. I think of the birthdays, imagined scenes with possible playmates, and other people's children who may have been about the same age as my baby. Our daughters (the baby's half-siblings), the holidays, and friends' conversations remind me. Doctors' registration forms, pro-life posters, and simply days gone by haunt me. There are frequent, endless reminders, but there are no sympathy cards, no understanding hugs, no casseroles for the grieving, no funerals, and no shoulders on which to cry.

Some of our choices have everlasting consequences. Time doesn't fully heal the wounds of death, regardless of the circumstances, but with God's grace, I have learned to live with the wounds.

My sister is in heaven. My father is in heaven. My baby is in heaven. I will never see them again during my earthly lifetime, but someday I will go to them.

*Blessed are those who mourn, for they will be comforted.*
Matthew 5:4

## Grieving the Loss

What is grief or grieving?

_______________________________________________

_______________________________________________

_______________________________________________

If you or someone you know has experienced the death of a close family member, please note how grief felt (either to you or the person you know). Note also how you (or the person you know) eventually worked through such grief. (Perhaps you might call the person you know who has faced grief and ask these questions.)

_______________________________________________

_______________________________________________

_______________________________________________

Upon viewing the gravesite of Lazarus, Jesus wept (John 11:36). Grief should be accepted, acknowledged, and responded to; but some deny it, refuse to acknowledge it, and drive their feelings deep beneath the surface. Describe the many ways people express grief.

_______________________________________________

_______________________________________________

_______________________________________________

In our society today, what are the common steps taken in the days, weeks, and months following the death of a loved one? Try to be specific.

_______________________________________________

_______________________________________________

_______________________________________________

What do people do to show their support to someone who is grieving the loss of a loved one?

*Death of a parent is death of the past. Death of a spouse is death of the present. Death of a child is death of the future.*[8]
– Unknown

What do you think the statement, "Death of a child is death of the future" means?

Following an abortion, a woman may face many losses in addition to the loss of the baby. Try to name them.

What support systems are in place in our current society to help a woman deal with her losses after her abortion?

## Bible Study

Mourning a death was given a great degree of significance in biblical times. Joseph's mourning of the death of his father, Jacob, is a good example. Please read Genesis 50:1-10.

8 Source unknown.

*Joseph threw himself upon his father and wept over him and kissed him. Then Joseph directed the physicians in his service to embalm his father Israel. So the physicians embalmed him, taking a full forty days, for that was the time required for embalming. And the Egyptians mourned for him seventy days.*

*When the days of mourning had passed, Joseph said to Pharaoh's court, "If I have found favor in your eyes, speak to Pharaoh for me. Tell him, 'My father made me swear an oath and said, "I am about to die; bury me in the tomb I dug for myself in the land of Canaan." Now let me go up and bury my father; then I will return.'"*

*Pharaoh said, "Go up and bury your father, as he made you swear to do."*

*So Joseph went up to bury his father. All Pharaoh's officials accompanied him – the dignitaries of his court and all the dignitaries of Egypt – besides all the members of Joseph's household and his brothers and those belonging to his father's household. Only their children and their flocks and herds were left in Goshen. Chariots and horsemen also went up with him. It was a very large company.*

*When they reached the threshing floor of Atad, near the Jordan, they lamented loudly and bitterly; and there Joseph observed a seven-day period of mourning for his father.*

Compare the days of mourning the death of Jacob with the common period of mourning in today's society. Do you believe our society today provides enough time, resources, and support for a person in mourning? Why or why not?

___

___

___

Following this biblical example, having ample opportunity to say good-bye to our lost, loved one is critical to our ultimate recovery from our grief. Identify ways that a woman suffering with grief as a result of an abortion can say good-bye to her baby.

__________________________________________________________

__________________________________________________________

__________________________________________________________

Please read together the third verse from Psalm 127.

> *Sons are a heritage from the Lord,*
> *Children a reward from him.*

In what ways could a child from an unintended pregnancy be a blessing?

__________________________________________________________

__________________________________________________________

__________________________________________________________

Through abortion, we have lost one of God's intended blessings. It is natural, and even logical, to grieve for a baby lost through abortion. Please read Isaiah 61:1-3.

> *The Spirit of the Sovereign Lord is on me,*
> *because the Lord has anointed me*
> *to preach good news to the poor.*
> *He has sent me to bind up the brokenhearted,*
> *to proclaim freedom for the captives*
> *and release from darkness for the prisoners,*
> *to proclaim the year of the Lord's favor*
> *and the day of vengeance of our God,*
> *to comfort all who mourn,*
> *and provide for those who grieve in Zion –*
> *to bestow on them a crown of beauty*
> *instead of ashes,*

*the oil of gladness*
*instead of mourning,*
*and a garment of praise*
*instead of a spirit of despair.*
*They will be called oaks of righteousness,*
*a planting of the Lord*
*for the display of his splendor.*

Based on these verses, who brings true comfort to us at times of mourning?

______________________________________________

______________________________________________

______________________________________________

How can we invoke his comforting support?

______________________________________________

______________________________________________

______________________________________________

King David mourned while his baby was ill. Upon hearing of the baby's death, he stopped mourning. Read aloud King David's explanation for this unusual response as written in 2 Samuel 12:21-23.

*His servants asked him, "Why are you acting this way? While the child was alive, you fasted and wept, but now that the child is dead, you get up and eat!"*

*He answered, "While the child was still alive, I fasted and wept. I thought, 'Who knows? The Lord may be gracious to me and let the child live.' But now that he is dead, why should I fast? Can I bring him back again? I will go to him, but he will not return to me."*

Upon the baby's death, David is quite certain the baby has gone to heaven. But David believes that he, too, will go to heaven. Recall the story about David and Bathsheba. What sins had David committed?

______________________________________________

______________________________________________

______________________________________________

Even with David's sins, he was confident he would someday "go to him," meaning he would go to heaven and see his child there. What do you think makes David so confident in his belief?

______________________________________________

______________________________________________

______________________________________________

God knows us, values us, and loves us even before we are born. He loves us here on earth and when we die. Children, babies, infants, and pre-born babies belong to him; and it is clear that when they leave this earth, they will live in heaven. We may not see our babies on earth ever again, but we will see them in heaven. Trust in the Lord. Have faith in his saving grace and forgiveness.

## Reflection & Encouragement

> *I did not know how hard it would be to say good-bye.*
> *Yet it was harder still, when I refused to say it.*
> – A grieving widow[9]

## Memory Verse

> *But those who hope in the Lord*
> *will renew their strength.*
> *They will soar on wings like eagles;*
> *they will run and not grow weary,*

9 Margaret K. Metzgar, M.A., LMHC, *A Time to Mourn, A Time to Dance: Help for the Losses in Life* (Appleton, WI: Thrivent Financial for Lutherans, 1995, 2011), 7.

*they will walk and not be faint.*
Isaiah 40:31

## Closing Prayer

Dear heavenly Father. Often we are so caught up in our own world and our own understanding of all that is in it that we do not recognize the blessings you have bestowed on us until perhaps it is too late. Children are one of your blessings, even when we believe the time, the place, or the circumstances are less than ideal. Forgive us, Lord, for not recognizing or appreciating all of your blessings. Now we find ourselves grieving our losses. Our grief creates feelings for us that are difficult to understand and painful to accept. Lord God, uphold us as we grieve and grant us peace. We thank you, dear Father, for your grace and steadfast love. Amen.

## Homework

- Place copies of the memory verse in convenient locations in your home and place of employment. Read it several times each day until you have committed it to memory.
- If you are participating in a small group study, read through Week 5 of the workbook to prepare for next week's meeting.
- List all the ways that having the baby, instead of choosing abortion, might have been a blessing to you or to others. At the end of the list, write boldly, "It is okay to miss this child. It is right to mourn this loss."
- Name your lost baby or babies and find a keepsake that can serve as a memorial (such as a cross, a pendant, or a picture for your wall).
- Write a eulogy, as used in a funeral, for your baby. Describe what his or her life would have been like based on your lost

hopes and dreams for him or her. Finish it with a statement professing your love for him or her.

- Cry, pray, rest quietly in prayerful meditation; seek the Lord's comfort and feel the loving touch of Jesus. Ask him to heal your grieving heart.

## Week 5

# Looking for Love along an Independent Path

*Peace I leave with you; my peace I give you. I do not give to you as the world gives. Do not let your hearts be troubled and do not be afraid.* – Jesus, John 14:27

### Opening Prayer

Dear Father God, thank you again for blessing us with your loving care this past week and today. Thank you for encouraging us to face our pasts, our fears, our failings, and our triumphs. The issues with which we struggle often overwhelm us. We do not want to face them alone, but with you and through your grace we know we can once again become whole. Draw near to us, oh Lord, as we draw near to you. We want to build our lives with you as our foundation, through Christ Jesus. Amen.

### Meeting & Greeting

*If you are working through this workbook on your own rather than participating in a small group study, please skip to the section entitled, "Looking for Love Along an Independent Path: A continuation of the author's story."*

Welcome to our fifth week in the *My Secret Loss* small group study. Thank you for continuing to support each other as we walk through the author's stories and relate them to ourselves, our family members, or our friends.

Today, tell us about something that was considered "cool" or "hot" or "groovy" or that "rocked" when you were in high school. Please include the decade to which your example refers, such as the 1970s or 1990s or 2000s. (Examples might involve clothing styles, fun activities, hair styles or colors, or more.)

______________________________

______________________________

______________________________

## Getting Started

Did anyone find a particularly meaningful way to memorialize their lost baby that you would like to share with the group?

______________________________

______________________________

______________________________

## Looking for Love along an Independent Path: A continuation of the author's story

*This section builds upon the author's initial story. For those participating in a small group study, please consider reading this piece aloud.*

A little over a year after my father's death, my mother remarried, and we moved to a new town, the town where my stepfather lived. We moved into his house, where he and two of his four children lived. His other children were grown and lived on their own. My oldest brother had since graduated from high school, so only my sister, my other brother, and I moved with my mother into this three-bedroom ranch house. The house was located in town. Living in this house was quite a change from our old house, which was a roomy, two-story farmhouse on 160 acres of land. To make more room, my stepfather finished a portion of the basement to add bedrooms for the boys. Even with the added bedrooms, the house felt very full.

In this full house, I learned to be independent, managing my life by myself with the help and advice of no one.

My sense of independence probably began much earlier, when as a young child I was required to play quietly due to a health condition. So I usually found myself playing alone. Later, with my father's death, we all had to become more independent to help our mother. She was busy trying to manage the house and our family business. Then with the move, my sense of independence solidified following the numerous, significant changes in our family, at church, and with friends.

After the move, we didn't see my oldest brother very often. He rarely visited this new house. Instead, he'd stay with our grandparents in our old hometown when he went "home" on college breaks. My other brother virtually lived in the basement of this new house, staying either in his bedroom or in the family room down there. It was too cold in the basement for me, so I rarely went down there. My sister, being four years older than I, seemed to view me as a pest. I was perpetually in her way as I was regularly reminded that I needed to give her some space. This wasn't easy considering we had to share a bedroom, and it was a very small bedroom. I'll never forget the line of masking tape she put straight down the middle of the room, which claimed for her one-half of the bed, the larger dresser, and the closet. Fortunately for me, I still got half of the bed, a small dresser, and access to the door.

Our new stepsister and stepbrother were similar in age to my sister and brother. We didn't know them very well before our parents got married, having met them only a few times. It probably was not easy for them to suddenly have to share their once comfortable home with four new people. It took only a short time before sibling rivalry and territory disputes were like an infectious disease. Arguments ensued over household chores, use of the bathroom, time on the phone, friends, the rules of the house, and more. My mother was often drained by her expanded role as referee.

I learned that the way to survive in this full house was to hide. Silent independence became my defense and protection. *Stay out of everyone's way and don't say a word*, I'd remind myself. It seemed best to avoid talking to anyone. Since I couldn't hide in my bedroom because my sister needed her space, I ultimately found it was easiest to hide in the living room by reading. Even there, I wasn't protected from the regular taunting about being a bookworm. *Just ignore everyone and they will leave me alone*, I'd remind myself.

In this new town, going to church was also different. Unlike our old hometown which had only one church which was attended by almost everyone in town, we now went to one of the smallest churches in town. Going to church wasn't much fun anymore now that I didn't have many friends at the church. Most of the really cool kids went to one of the big Catholic churches in town. I wasn't included in any of their church activities. I began to question the purpose for going to church, and I questioned the value of the Bible. *If God was in a faraway heaven with all the people who had died, then why bother going to church?* I'd wonder. As for the Bible, I didn't understand how the old stories could have anything to do with life today. I had no idea that one could have a relationship of love with God.

> *When we are living apart from God, we can be lonely and lost, even in the midst of a crowd.* – Billy Graham[10]

Ultimately, our full house became a lonesome place, as did our church. So I found myself longing for more and more social interaction with friends. It seemed there were never enough things to do or enough places to go. I made a number of new friends in the new town, but it didn't seem like enough. I always wanted more friends and more things to do. I remember how my heart would leap when the phone rang, hoping someone was calling to invite me to do something with them. I also remember the feelings of disappointment when I learned the call was

10 Connie Wetzell and Criswell Freeman, *God's Survival Guide For Women* (Nashville, TN: Elm Hill Books, imprint of J. Countryman®, a division of Thomas Nelson, Inc., 2005), 172.

for someone else. So, I continued to seek more friends, more fun, and more independence.

On this quest, I began to take my cues from the world around me. During this time in my life, there were a lot of social and political changes in the United States. It was a time of political rebellion over the Vietnam War. It was the beginning of the women's liberation movement, a time when women were fighting for equal rights at work and in their homes. Young people everywhere sought freedom from the strict, conformist norms of our recent past society.

This same time frame was also known as the Sexual Revolution. According to the world around me, the concept of freedom included sexual freedom. There were news reports of communal living and outdoor rock concerts whose attendees were often high on drugs and scantily dressed (some nude), freely expressing their love for each other. Prompted by new forms of birth control and the Supreme Court decision of *Roe v. Wade* making abortion lawful, sexual freedom was often touted as an equal right for men and for women. The risks of an unplanned pregnancy were minimized. Women had choices and the right to make these choices. Sexual choice meant freedom and equality.

The old boundaries regarding relationships were supposedly not as relevant anymore. The signals I received were confusing. I was intrigued by what I saw on television and in the news. I believed in freedom and equality. I didn't know what it all meant or how one was supposed to manage all those freedoms and develop healthy relationships. But in my independent way, I believed I could and should figure out these questions on my own.

I didn't realize it, but I was searching for love along an independent path. I didn't consult with my mother, siblings, or friends. I longed to fill a void in my heart, but I didn't understand how to do it. I didn't even understand what was truly causing the void in my heart. I didn't have Christ as my foundation, and I didn't know it was a relationship with him that I was missing.

Without the advantage of wise counsel from the people closest to me, I assumed the teachings of the world were accurate, at least to some degree. Having only a far-away God, I didn't understand his intended plan for relationships. So with the wrong pressures from the wrong guy, I accepted a worldly path to find the love I sought.

I made mistakes by not standing up for myself and by not saying no. I was on the wrong path but didn't know how to turn things around. I had gotten in too deep.

When I learned I was pregnant, I couldn't face the losses I envisioned. Without a strong foundation in Christ for my life, I desperately needed my friends and my family. The thought of losing any of these relationships created for me an intolerable, unimaginable future. It was only natural that I clung tightly to these relationships, considering I didn't know to draw true strength from God.

So I continued to listen to the teachings of the world. It's just tissue. It's not a living baby. It is legal. It is your only choice.

> *Do not love the world or anything in the world. If anyone loves the world, the love of the Father is not in him. For everything in the world – the cravings of sinful man, the lust of his eyes and the boasting of what he has and does – comes not from the Father but from the world. The world and its desires pass away, but the man who does the will of God lives forever.* 1 John 2:15-17

## Putting It in Context

What loving relationships were changed for the author when her family moved to the new town?

____________________________________________

____________________________________________

____________________________________________

Can you think of times in your life in which some of your loving relationships were severed or altered? What did you do in response to these changes? Did these changes have a positive influence or a negative influence on your life in the end? Why?

________________________________________________________

________________________________________________________

________________________________________________________

Why are relationships with other people so important to us?

________________________________________________________

________________________________________________________

________________________________________________________

The author confused freedom and independence as taught by the world with happiness. What do you think were the real desires of her heart?

________________________________________________________

________________________________________________________

________________________________________________________

What were the influences of the world in your life (or the life of your friend or family member) at the time of your (her) unintended pregnancy?

________________________________________________________

________________________________________________________

________________________________________________________

Do you think the author's feelings and choices would have been different if she had a close relationship with God? Explain.

________________________________________________________

________________________________________________________

________________________________________________________

Does a close relationship with God guarantee that we will not make mistakes in our relationships or in the choices we make? Why or why not? (Perhaps you will recall the story of David and Bathsheba when considering this question.)

---

---

---

*Now the Lord is the Spirit, and where the Spirit of the Lord is, there is freedom.* 2 Corinthians 3:17

## Bible Study

Please read Romans 12:2.

*Do not conform any longer to the pattern of this world, but be transformed by the renewing of your mind. Then you will be able to test and approve what God's will is – his good, pleasing and perfect will.*

The Bible states we should not look to the things of the world to learn our direction. What do we learn about relationships from television, movies, and magazines today?

---

---

---

What other things might we learn today from television, in the news, or from the world around us that would likely not be pleasing to God?

---

---

---

This Bible verse suggests we should become transformed by renewing our minds. What can we do to renew our minds and learn what God's will is for our lives?

---

---

---

The author didn't have a close relationship with God when she was a teenager. This passage describes our relationships with God. Please read aloud, 1 John 4:7-16.

> *Dear friends, let us love one another, for love comes from God. Everyone who loves has been born of God and knows God. Whoever does not love does not know God, because God is love. This is how God showed his love among us: He sent his one and only Son into the world that we might live through him. This is love, not that we loved God, but that he loved us and sent his Son as an atoning sacrifice for our sins. Dear friends, since God so loved us, we also ought to love one another. No one has ever seen God; but if we love one another, God lives in us and his love is made complete in us.*
>
> *We know that we live in him and he in us, because he has given us of his Spirit. And we have seen and testify that the Father has sent his Son to be the Savior of the world. If anyone acknowledges that Jesus is the Son of God, God lives in him and he in God. And so we know and rely on the love God has for us.*
>
> *God is love. Whoever lives in love lives in God, and God in him.*

Based on this passage, what is God like?

---

---

---

How do we know God loves us?

______________________________________________

______________________________________________

______________________________________________

How do we draw God near to us?

______________________________________________

______________________________________________

______________________________________________

What is love? (You may want to look up 1 Corinthians 13:4-8 for a biblical definition.)

______________________________________________

______________________________________________

______________________________________________

> *Jesus replied, "If anyone loves me, he will obey my teaching. My Father will love him, and we will come to him and make our home with him." John 14:23*

When we have a relationship with God through Jesus, how closely involved will he be in our lives?

______________________________________________

______________________________________________

______________________________________________

Please read what Jesus said in Matthew 7:24-27.

> *Therefore everyone who hears these words of mine and puts them into practice is like a wise man who built his house on the rock. The rain came down, the streams rose, and the*

> *winds blew and beat against that house; yet it did not fall, because it had its foundation on the rock. But everyone who hears these words of mine and does not put them into practice is like a foolish man who built his house on sand. The rain came down, the streams rose, and the winds blew and beat against that house, and it fell with a great crash.*

What happens to a home when the foundation breaks, cracks, or crumbles?

____________________________________________

____________________________________________

____________________________________________

How do we build a strong foundation for our lives?

____________________________________________

____________________________________________

____________________________________________

## Reflection & Encouragement

> *O Christ, in Thee my soul hath found,*
> *And found in Thee alone,*
> *The peace, the joy I sought so long,*
> *The bliss till now unknown.*
> *I sighed for rest and happiness,*
> *I yearned for them, not Thee;*
> *But while I passed my Saviour by,*
> *His love laid hold on me.*
> *Now none but Christ can satisfy,*
> *None other name for me;*
> *There's love, and life, and lasting joy,*
> *Lord Jesus, found in Thee.*
> *– Author unknown.*[11]

11 Stephen Ross, compiler, "Quotes and Notes," *Wholesome Words*, 9 December 2005, No. 2,

## Memory Verse

*Trust in the Lord and do good;*
*dwell in the land and enjoy safe pasture.*
*Delight yourself in the Lord*
*and he will give you the desires of your heart.*
Psalm 37:3-4

## Closing Prayer

Dear Lord, you said the truth will set us free. We are bound by our sins, living with guilt and often shame. We cannot set ourselves free. We seek love and acceptance from people, places, and things in the world that neither last nor reflect your love. We remain vulnerable and lost. You, Lord, are the truth. We ask you to come into our lives, forgive us for our sins and set us free. You are our savior. Only through you, Lord Jesus, can we truly know God's love. We pray with sincere gratefulness for your everlasting love, grace, and mercy. Amen.

## Homework

- Place copies of the memory verse in convenient locations in your home and place of employment. Read it several times each day until you have committed it to memory.
- If you are participating in a small group study, please read through Week 6 of the workbook to prepare for next week's meeting.
- In a journal or notebook, write your answers to the following questions:
    1. Describe your relationships with your family, friends, and the father of your baby just prior to your unintended pregnancy. Did you feel vulnerable or insecure in any of

*www.wholesomewords.org/poetry/mylord.html#OCIT,* citing "Copied from the back of the title page of *James Gilmour of Mongolia: his diaries, letters, and reports,* edited by Richard Lovett, 1893 ed."

these relationships? If so, in what ways did your feelings of vulnerability or insecurity impact your decisions?

2. Describe your relationship with God just prior to your unintended pregnancy.

3. Do you think your choices would have been any different at the time of your unintended pregnancy if your relationship with God had been stronger? Why or why not?

Week 6

# Heroic Measures

*For the wages of sin is death, but the gift of God is eternal life in Christ Jesus our Lord.* Romans 6:23

## Opening Prayer

Again dear Father in heaven, we are here with you, exploring our hearts and our choices of days gone by, of this day, and of days to come. We find ourselves weak and weary from carrying the burden of our mistakes day after day. Help us, dear Father, to find relief. Only through you, by the death and resurrection of your son, Jesus Christ, will we have the strength to face our mistakes and to set our burdens down. We thank you, dear Father, for your steadfast love and faithfulness. Amen.

## Meeting & Greeting

*If you are working through this workbook on your own rather than participating in a small group study, please skip to the section entitled, "Heroic Measures: A continuation of the author's story."*

Welcome to our sixth week in the *My Secret Loss* small group study.

This week, tell us about a person you admire and describe one of the reasons you admire him or her.

## Getting Started

Please share your opinions on how having Christ's love as your life's foundation can impact your relationships and your decisions.

## Heroic Measures: A continuation of the author's story

*This section builds upon the author's initial story. Please consider reading this piece aloud.*

I had volunteered to work at our church-sponsored thrift shop, but over the weekend, I fell off a step ladder while washing windows. I broke my foot. I hated to cancel at the thrift shop, knowing that canceling with such short notice would put the coordinator in a bind. Just as I was about to make that call and cancel, my daughter said, "Don't worry about it Mom. I'll take your place."

She took my place.

We've all taken someone's place to help them out. We've all had someone take our place when we needed a hand. Often, the situation is as simple as volunteering at the local thrift shop, doing a small chore, or running an errand. But sometimes it involves something as critical as an organ transplant between family members, where one person literally gives up a part of herself to another. The organ of the first person takes the place of the dying organ of the second person so the second person might live.

I'm sure you've read about heroic stories in the newspapers where one person puts himself in danger in order to save the life of another. Perhaps while walking down the street, the story's hero notices a child wandering out into traffic. Instantly, the hero dives in front of the oncoming car to shove the child to safety. Our hero takes the child's place without regard to his own life. Similar stories involve our firefighters, police officers, and people in the armed forces. It is their responsibility to step into danger to save another person or an entire nation from harm. The events of September 11, 2001, are filled with heroic stories like these.

I know of a time when someone took my place without regard to his own life. It happened a very long time ago. It happened before I even knew I needed help.

Throughout my life, I had made a number of choices that could have been better. In hindsight, as I compare my life against God's will and his commands, I find myself guilty. I am guilty of doing wrong and making mistakes. I fail to act out of love and make wrong choices out of fear of the reactions of other people. I make poor choices out of a desire for acceptance from others in my life. I fail to act or speak up when I see an injustice and fail in many more ways. If all my failures were highlighted and listed here, we would likely discover I have managed to violate every one of the Ten Commandments, whether in my thoughts or through my actions or my inactions. Each and every one of these sins carries the same penalty, eternal death. Although no sin is worse than another, I carry the burden of killing most closely to my heart.

It is an extremely heavy burden.

Thinking about my abortion today, I struggle to see any difference in that choice and a choice to hire a hit man to eliminate an innocent life. In each case, someone is paid to take the life of another. Am I guilty of murder or perhaps conspiracy to commit murder? Did I kill? I believe so, and it is a heavy burden to carry in my heart.

God commands us, saying, "You shall not kill." Killing is sin. The penalty for all sin is death. The penalty for killing is death, the same penalty as for any other violation of God's commands. For years I walked along death row, perhaps not fully understanding what my destiny was to be. I knew many of my choices were not good choices, so I tried to make up for them by living life properly. But I couldn't be perfect. No matter what I tried, it was impossible for me to live a sin-free life.

As a result, for over thirty years, I was driving at full speed down a winding road toward death, under an eternal death sentence. Try as I might, I couldn't change the course. I couldn't fix the steering or the brakes in order to get off the road upon which I was traveling. I could do nothing on my own to change the ultimate outcome.

Over those thirty years, God kept pulling at my heart. He put people along the road to remind me of his presence, his love, and his path for forgiveness. He blessed me with a husband who walked hand-in-hand with me along my faith journey, never pushing too hard and never pulling me off the path. He blessed us with our daughters and placed upon our hearts the importance of modeling godly lives so they might come to know the Lord. Through our desire to teach them, God continued to teach us. He brought Christian friends into our lives – people whom I knew had something of true value in their hearts, even though I did not fully understand what it was. God drew me closer to him through these people until I finally and unexpectedly caught on.

Jesus is the one who took my place on my road to an eternal death. He paid the price for my crimes, my countless violations of God's commands. He paid the price for the choices that weighed me down with shame, so I might live again. He took my place without regard to his own life. And all I had to do was to have faith, tell him what I had done, repent, and ask him to help me. In my mind's eye, I can picture him standing at the edge of the cliff of death, holding out his hand, and stopping my careening car with unimaginable strength and love, just before it flies over the rocky ledge of death. He humbly opens the car door, tells me to get out because he will take it from here. He gets in the car, and it rolls over the edge.

He took my place. He is my hero.

He took your place too. He is our Savior. This is truth.

*For you, O Lord, have delivered my soul from death,*
*my eyes from tears,*
*my feet from stumbling,*

*that I may walk before the Lord*
*in the land of the living.*
Psalm 116:8-9

## He Took My Place

Can you describe a time when someone took your place to help you out with something? How did it make you feel?

In describing her symbolic ride in the car towards an eternal death, the author claims there was nothing she could do on her own that would enable her to stop the car or to steer it onto another road. What do you think she meant?

The author looks back and finds that God has placed people in her path to draw her closer to him. Who do you think God has put in your life to draw you closer to him?

What do you think the author may have noticed that made her believe her Christian friends had something of real value in their hearts that she didn't believe she had?

_______________________________________________

_______________________________________________

> *He himself bore our sins in his body on the tree, so that we might die to sins and live for righteousness; by his wounds you have been healed.* 1 Peter 2:24

## Bible Study

In his letter to the Romans, Paul explains how Jesus, being fully righteous, can take the place of all of us. Read Romans 5:18-19.

> *Consequently, just as the result of one trespass was condemnation for all men, so also the result of one act of righteousness was justification that brings life for all men. For just as through the disobedience of the one man the many were made sinners, so also through the obedience of the one man the many will be made righteous.*

What does it mean when it says the "result of one act of righteousness was justification that brings life for all men?"

_______________________________________________

_______________________________________________

_______________________________________________

"Through the obedience of one man the many will be made righteous." What do you think this means?

_______________________________________________

_______________________________________________

_______________________________________________

It is never too late to turn your life over to God. Please read the following parable as told by Jesus in Luke 15:11-24.

*Jesus continued: "There was a man who had two sons. The younger one said to his father, 'Father, give me my share of the estate.' So he divided his property between them.*

*"Not long after that, the younger son got together all he had, set off for a distant country and there squandered his wealth in wild living. After he had spent everything, there was a severe famine in that whole country, and he began to be in need. So he went and hired himself out to a citizen of that country, who sent him to his fields to feed pigs. He longed to fill his stomach with the pods that the pigs were eating, but no one gave him anything.*

*"When he came to his senses, he said, 'How many of my father's hired men have food to spare, and here I am starving to death! I will set out and go back to my father and say to him: Father, I have sinned against heaven and against you. I am no longer worthy to be called your son; make me like one of your hired men.' So he got up and went to his father.*

*But while he was still a long way off, his father saw him and was filled with compassion for him; he ran to his son, threw his arms around him and kissed him.*

*"The son said to him, 'Father, I have sinned against heaven and against you. I am no longer worthy to be called your son.'*

*"But the father said to his servants, 'Quick! Bring the best robe and put it on him. Put a ring on his finger and sandals on his feet. Bring the fattened calf and kill it. Let's have a feast and celebrate. For this son of mine was dead and is alive again; he was lost and is found.' So they began to celebrate."*

The son had been in many unpleasant places in the parable. What unpleasant places (whether physical, relational, behavioral, or emotional places) do you believe are common to women who have had abortions?

If you feel comfortable, please share the unpleasant places you have been as a result of your unintended pregnancy or your abortion.

______________________________________________

______________________________________________

______________________________________________

Why do you think the father in the parable was so happy to see his son return even after all of the disrespectful and wasteful things he did?

______________________________________________

______________________________________________

______________________________________________

God wants us to turn back to him. He loves us and is waiting to forgive us. Both the parable and the author's story describe ways used by God to encourage us to return to him. Describe them.

______________________________________________

______________________________________________

______________________________________________

What other ways might God use to encourage us to turn to him?

______________________________________________

______________________________________________

______________________________________________

If we wander away from God but later "come to our senses" and decide to return to him, at what point will he reach out to us?

______________________________________________

______________________________________________

______________________________________________

Describe how "coming home" to your heavenly Father could change your life or the life of someone who has not been walking closely with God.

_______________________________________________

_______________________________________________

_______________________________________________

*The Lord is gracious and righteous;*
*our God is full of compassion.*
*The Lord protects the simplehearted;*
*when I was in great need, he saved me.*
Psalm 116:5-6

As we study this week's chapter, consider whether you are absolutely certain you have a relationship with God through Jesus Christ. If you have wandered away from him or never known a personal relationship with him, he is longing to run to you and take you in his arms. If you have any doubt that you have accepted what Jesus did on the cross personally for your sins and if you're not one hundred percent sure you have received his free gift of eternal life, this is where to start to experience true peace. If you will but pray a simple prayer like this, from your heart, God has promised to save you.

*Dear Lord, I acknowledge that I have not followed your way. I ask now for you to forgive me of all my sins. I believe you willingly died on the cross for my sins, rose again, and reign as my Savior; I thank you that I am now pure in your sight because of what you, Lord Jesus, did on the cross for me. You love me like no other and desire to come into my life. I accept your gift of salvation. Guide me, Lord, and grant me peace. Thank you. In Jesus' name I pray. Amen.*

If you just prayed this prayer of salvation for the first time, all of heaven is rejoicing! God has saved you from your sin; he loves you and is with you! He has come into your life and will never leave you (Hebrews 13:5). This is the most crucial decision you can make because not only will your new relationship with Christ influence your life on earth, but it will also assure you of eternal life (1 John 5:12).

## Reflection & Encouragement

God has promised he will remove our transgressions as far as the east is from the west (Psalm 103:12). The distance from east to west may not seem very far when you're standing on the Continental Divide, and the east is right next to the west. So the scope of God's forgiveness is better explained when you think of embarking on an airline flight to the west. If you start flying west, you can continue in that direction without ever reaching the east. No matter how long you fly toward the west and no matter how many times you circle the globe, you will never be heading east. If you took a flight north, you would eventually hit the North Pole and then start heading south. At that point, north meets south. God didn't say our sins have been removed as far as the north is from the south. When he spoke of his unlimited love and forgiveness, he used the earth's latitude, not longitude.[12]

## Memory Verse

> *Though your sins are like scarlet, they shall be as white as snow; though they are red as crimson, they shall be like wool.*
> Isaiah 1:18

## Closing Prayer

> Dear Lord Jesus, how can we begin to thank you for your loving grace? Thank you for taking our places so we do not need to face the penalty of death for our choices of yesterday, today, and tomorrow. We are deeply grateful. Your selfless act of love for all of mankind is unsurpassed. You are our Lord and Savior. We ask you to keep us and guide us through all of our days,

12 Jim Nicodem, "The Father Heart of God," *Preaching Today*, Tape 152, as quoted in Raymond McHenry, *McHenry's Stories for the Soul* (Peabody, MA: Hendrickson Publishers, 2001), 117.

so through our thoughts, our words, and our actions, we will honor you. Amen.

## Homework

- Place copies of the memory verse in convenient locations in your home and place of employment. Read it several times each day until you have committed it to memory.
- If you are participating in a small group study, please read through Week 7 of the workbook to prepare for next week's meeting.
- In your journal, make a list of all the regrets you have regarding your choices leading to your unintended pregnancy and your decision to have an abortion.
- Also in your journal or notebook, describe all regrettable things you have done since your abortion, noting particularly those things you believe might have been caused in part by your choice to have an abortion.
- In your prayers, read these lists to God, telling him you want to be forgiven for your regrettable choices. Ask God to help you find your way back to his home and enable you to know his forgiveness.

# Week 7

# I Don't Feel Forgiven

*I have swept away your offenses like a cloud,*
*your sins like the morning mist. Return to me,*
*for I have redeemed you.* Isaiah 44:22

## Opening Prayer

Dear Lord, our Father in heaven, each day as the sun rises and then sets again, we marvel at the beauty of your creation and the gifts you have given us. You know what we need each day, and we know you lovingly provide for us in every way. We often feel unworthy of your love and, therefore, find it hard to open our hearts to your everlasting grace. Help us to understand it is not our worthiness that makes you love us, but it is your love that makes us worthy. We thank you dear Father for loving us. Amen.

## Meeting & Greeting

*If you are working through this workbook on your own rather than participating in a small group study, please skip to the section entitled, "Getting Started."*

Welcome to our seventh week in this *My Secret Loss* small group study.

Please tell us about something you remember doing wrong as a young child that you tried to hide from your parents.

______________________________________________

______________________________________________

______________________________________________

## Getting Started

List a number of regrets you believe women might have about their choices leading to their unintended pregnancies and their abortions.

______________________________________________

______________________________________________

______________________________________________

## I Don't Feel Forgiven: A continuation of the author's story

*This section builds upon the author's initial story. For those participating in a small group study, a volunteer is invited to read this section aloud.*

I recall cradling our first infant daughter in my arms. She was such a beautiful baby with a tuft of auburn-brown hair on the top of her head, a small turned-up nose, and eyes that seemed to look deeply into my heart. On this particular day, she was about two months old. She weighed about eleven pounds. She was so tiny, so dependent, and yet so demanding.

"Colic," they said.

If only she would fall asleep. She cried and cried and cried. I felt so helpless. My heart would break for her as I tried to comfort her to no avail. I changed her position to an upright position, hoping she would rest her head on my shoulder. I patted her back. I lightly bounced as I walked. She still cried. She cried so deeply; she seemed to be crying from her toes. As she cried, she'd look at me with eyes that pleaded for comfort.

I sat down. I again cradled her in my arms. I rocked in the chair. She wouldn't calm down. I couldn't seem to help her.

Minutes felt like hours. She cried and cried. My heart would break for her, as I wanted more than anything to be able to comfort her. I wished she could understand how much I loved her. I wished she knew she was safe in my arms. I wanted her to rest.

Eventually, she began to wear down. Her eyes looked sleepy. Her eyelids slipped closed. But in a moment, she snapped her eyes open again. Then she would cry again. In time, her eyelids drooped, but she again opened them quickly, fighting to stay awake. Over and over she repeated this process.

I gently touched her forehead with my fingertips, quietly singing a lullaby, trying to lull her to sleep. I slid my fingertips down her forehead, past her eyes, and onto her pink cheeks. Her eyelids closed as my fingers passed over them. Finally, her eyes stayed closed. She was asleep.

I gazed both in silent relief and in awe at her beautiful, blackish-brown eyelashes against her porcelain skin. As I watched her sleep, I imagined a little halo forming over the top of her head. She was my little angel. She was my blessing from God. I loved her in a way I never knew possible.

I loved her at all times: when she ate, when she slept, when she cried, when she burped, when she got a bath, and when she woke me in the night. I loved her even when she exhausted me. I loved her unconditionally. I loved her with that 1 Corinthians 13 kind of love: love that is patient and kind; love that is not jealous, boastful or rude; love that is not easily angered and which keeps no record of wrongs; love that does not delight in evil but rejoices with the truth; and love that always protects, always hopes, and always perseveres.

Like my colicky daughter, I have cried for comfort time and time again; yet I was unable or unwilling to recognize that God was and will always be my comforter. He loves me as his child. I can call him Father.

God heard my many cries over the years. He watched as I failed to realize he was just a prayer away. He waited for me as I sought love and acceptance from other sources. With heartfelt pain and love, he was there when I gave my baby to him through abortion. He watched me run from my guilt and live with my shame. Once I found the path to his door, God forgave me. He was there as I pleaded for comfort, and yet I doubted his word.

Every time I prayed for forgiveness, I specifically prayed to be forgiven for my choice to have an abortion. Over and over, year after year, I'd pray for the same thing. The choice to have an abortion had become an unforgivable sin in my heart. I could not distinguish between my earlier choice to have an abortion and my now repentant heart following that choice. With society's strong anti-abortion messages, I felt only shame. I felt shame without the possibility of forgiveness.

I couldn't believe forgiveness was possible for abortion. Forgiveness wasn't available for someone like me. I wasn't worthy. Even though, intellectually, everything pointed to forgiveness and said God had forgiven me, I could not accept it. The feelings of guilt and shame remained. The need to hide my choice remained. I heard God's words of love, but I couldn't accept them as truth.

> *Forget the former things; do not dwell on the past.*
> Isaiah 43:18

Then one day, the words of the Bible began to shine through my doubts, my shame, and my feelings of unworthiness. I discovered I did not need to be worthy. I learned that we are all unworthy, but God loves us anyway. I was convinced when I finally realized I was a child of God and he loves me unconditionally even more than I am capable of loving my daughters.

The Bible says God is love. His love is the 1 Corinthians 13 kind of love. His love is greater than the love of a mother or father for a child. His love is a gift to me. I didn't do anything to deserve his love. In fact, the opposite is true. I am so happy God doesn't give me what I deserve. Instead, he lavishes his love on me and he forgives me. Through faith I am forgiven. Only through faith can I be healed.

> *For God so loved the world that he gave his one and only Son, that whoever believes in him shall not perish but have eternal life.* John 3:16

## God Is Love

Newborns are totally dependent upon their parents for care. They are incapable of giving anything back to their parents in appreciation until that magic age when they learn how to smile. Yet parents love their newborn infants and give them everything they need. How are we like the newborn in God's eyes?

________________________________________

________________________________________

________________________________________

What correlation can be drawn between a mother's love for her infant son or daughter and God's love for each of us?

________________________________________

________________________________________

________________________________________

In 1 John 4:16, John states that God is love. Review what love is, as defined in the Bible in 1 Corinthians 13:4-8, which was paraphrased above in the author's story. What, then, do we know about God's character when we say God is love?

________________________________________

________________________________________

________________________________________

What, if anything, does one do to become worthy of God's love and forgiveness?

---

---

---

## Bible Study

God is love and he is our Father. We know this is true by what we read in Romans 8:15-17.

> *For you did not receive a spirit that makes you a slave again to fear, but you received the Spirit of sonship. And by him we cry, "Abba, Father." The Spirit himself testifies with our spirit that we are God's children. Now if we are children, then we are heirs – heirs of God and co-heirs with Christ, if indeed we share in his sufferings in order that we may also share in his glory.*

Some Bible translations use the word *adoption* rather than *sonship*. Discuss what it means to be adopted as a son or daughter into another family.

---

---

---

This Bible passage describes us as adopted daughters in God's family, heirs of God and co-heirs with Christ. What does it mean to be an heir to a family estate? What does this mean for us to be co-heirs with Christ? Please read John 1:12-13.

---

---

---

> *Yet to all who received him, to those who believed in his name, he gave the right to become children of God – children*

*born not of natural descent, nor of human decision or a husband's will, but born of God.*

When an orphaned child is adopted into a family, does the child do anything in particular to earn the right to be adopted? For example, does the child need to have some kind of dowry, bank account, or specific talent? Does the child first need to prove that he or she can behave properly or do well in school?

___

___

___

How is the adoption of an orphaned child similar to our adoption into God's family?

___

___

___

The above passage in John 1 states that we need to receive Christ and believe in him to become children of God. How would an orphaned child receive the love of her new parents? How do we receive the love of Christ?

___

___

___

Some orphaned children are teenagers, who after years of being shuffled from foster home to foster home feel abandoned, neglected, and angry. Ultimately, this translates to believing they are unlovable and unworthy. When a new family reaches out to them, they refuse them and their love, even after being brought into their home to live. How might this be similar to some of us and our feelings about God's love and forgiveness?

___

___

___

Please read the following story about Jesus from Luke 7:36-50.

> *Now one of the Pharisees invited Jesus to have dinner with him, so he went to the Pharisee's house and reclined at the table. When a woman who had lived a sinful life in that town learned that Jesus was eating at the Pharisee's house, she brought an alabaster jar of perfume, and as she stood behind him at his feet weeping, she began to wet his feet with her tears. Then she wiped them with her hair, kissed them and poured perfume on them.*
>
> *When the Pharisee who had invited him saw this, he said to himself, "If this man were a prophet, he would know who is touching him and what kind of woman she is – that she is a sinner."*
>
> *Jesus answered him, "Simon, I have something to tell you."*
>
> *"Tell me, teacher," he said.*
>
> *"Two men owed money to a certain moneylender. One owed him five hundred denarii, and the other fifty. Neither of them had the money to pay him back, so he canceled the debts of both. Now which of them will love him more?"*
>
> *Simon replied, "I suppose the one who had the bigger debt canceled."*
>
> *"You have judged correctly," Jesus said.*
>
> *Then he turned toward the woman and said to Simon, "Do you see this woman? I came into your house. You did not give me any water for my feet, but she wet my feet with her tears and wiped them with her hair. You did not give me a kiss, but this woman, from the time I entered, has not*

*stopped kissing my feet. You did not put oil on my head, but she has poured perfume on my feet. Therefore, I tell you, her many sins have been forgiven – for she loved much. But he who has been forgiven little loves little."*

*Then Jesus said to her, "Your sins are forgiven."*

*The other guests began to say among themselves, "Who is this who even forgives sins?"*

*Jesus said to the woman, "Your faith has saved you; go in peace."*

Compare the woman in the above story with a post-abortive woman. What similarities might exist?

______________________________________________

______________________________________________

______________________________________________

What exactly did this woman do when she turned to Jesus? What do you think were the feelings of her heart?

______________________________________________

______________________________________________

______________________________________________

Do you think Jesus measures our sins or our heart? Explain.

______________________________________________

______________________________________________

______________________________________________

Following the lead of the woman in this story, what must we do in order to receive Jesus' love and forgiveness?

______________________________________________

______________________________________________

______________________________________________

Jesus told his disciples a parable about an unjust judge. He contrasts this judge against God. Ask a volunteer to read this parable from Luke 18:2-8.

> *He said: "In a certain town there was a judge who neither feared God nor cared about men. And there was a widow in that town who kept coming to him with the plea, 'Grant me justice against my adversary.'*
>
> *"For some time he refused. But finally he said to himself, 'Even though I don't fear God or care about men, yet because this widow keeps bothering me, I will see that she gets justice, so that she won't eventually wear me out with her coming!'"*
>
> *And the Lord said, "Listen to what the unjust judge says. And will not God bring about justice for his chosen ones, who cry out to him day and night? Will he keep putting them off? I tell you, he will see that they get justice, and quickly. However, when the Son of Man comes, will he find faith on the earth?"*

In the author's story, she notes that prayer after prayer, year after year, she asked for God's forgiveness for her choice to have an abortion. If God is different from the unjust judge in the above story, did the author need to ask over and over and over for his forgiveness?

________________________________________

________________________________________

________________________________________

When are our prayers for forgiveness answered by God?

________________________________________

________________________________________

________________________________________

Please read what Jesus says in John 6:37-40.

> *All that the Father gives me will come to me, and whoever comes to me I will never drive away. For I have come down from heaven not to do my will but to do the will of him who sent me. And this is the will of him who sent me, that I shall lose none of all that he has given me, but raise them up at the last day. For my Father's will is that everyone who looks to the Son and believes in him shall have eternal life, and I will raise him up at the last day.*

Based on the above Bible passage, do you think Jesus ever turns his back on those who pray for his forgiveness? Why then do you think many women do not "feel" forgiven?

________________________________________

________________________________________

________________________________________

The following three passages tell us we can approach God with confidence, without doubt, and with complete faith that he will be there for us. Please read Hebrews 4:16, Psalm 50:15, and 1 John 5:14-15, which are written below respectively.

> *Let us then approach the throne of grace with confidence, so that we may receive mercy and find grace to help us in our time of need.*
>
> *And call upon me in the day of trouble;*
>
> *I will deliver you, and you will honor me.*
>
> *This is the confidence we have in approaching God: that if we ask anything according to his will, he hears us. And if we know that he hears us – whatever we ask – we know that we have what we asked of him.*

The Bible cannot be clearer. We are daughters of our heavenly Father. We do not have to be worthy. In fact, there is nothing we can do to make ourselves worthy. He has made us worthy through his love. God has adopted us. We only need to turn to him with a repentant heart and accept his love through faith. As his children, his daughters, we can go to him with confidence. He will not make us wait for his love. He will not make us earn his forgiveness. He will give to us as our loving Father.

Come sit with your Father in heaven. Tell him what you need. Let him love you. Accept his forgiveness. Love him in return.

## Reflection & Encouragement

> *To believe in God is the beginning. To hear Him call your name is the start. To dance in His arms is real life. The music will be fast, then slow, then fast. The steps will be both easy and complex. The lights will be sometimes bright and sometimes dim. But to miss Him and to miss the dance is to miss the life you were made for.* – Angela Thomas[13]

> *I think that if God forgives us we might forgive ourselves. Otherwise it is almost like setting up ourselves as a higher tribunal than Him.* – C. S. Lewis[14]

## Memory Verse

> *How great is the love the Father has lavished on us, that we should be called children of God! And that is what we are!*
> 1 John 3:1a

13 Angela Thomas, *Do You Think I'm Beautiful?* (Nashville, TN: Thomas Nelson, Inc., 2003), 28.

14 C. S. Lewis, *The Collected Letters of C. S. Lewis, Vol. III: Narnia, Cambridge, and Joy 1950-1963*, ed. Walter Hooper (San Francisco: Harper Collins, 2007), 109.

## Closing Prayer

Dear Father, our loving Abba, how great is your love that you have lavished on us that we should be called your children. We thank you for welcoming us into your family, for accepting us as your daughters. Your love is incomprehensible to us. Forgive us for our doubts, for our lack of understanding, and for our weak faith. Strengthen our faith through your Holy Spirit so we will always know your love for us. We don't want to miss you or your love for us. Enable our hearts and our minds to accept your love and your forgiveness. We pray these things in Jesus' name. Amen.

## Homework

- Place copies of the memory verse in convenient locations in your home and place of employment. Read it several times each day until you have committed it to memory.
- If you are participating in a small group, read through Week 8 of the workbook to prepare for next week's meeting.
- Have you refused to accept God's love and forgiveness? Have you failed to believe in his love for you? If so, list in your journal or notebook as many reasons you can think of for this refusal.
- In your journal or notebook, imagine and list the traits of the most perfect father. Compare these traits with the definition of love in 1 Corinthians 13:4-8.
- Remember God is the God of gods and King of kings, and you are his daughter. You are a princess in God's family. You are his heir. Read Galatians 5:22. What are the benefits of living a life with Christ?
- Pray, asking God to open your heart so you can receive his love in faith. Ask him to remove your doubts, Satan's lies, from your heart.

## Week 8

# Let It Go! Forgive Them

*Refrain from anger and turn from wrath; do not fret – it leads only to evil.* Psalm 37:8

### Opening Prayer

Dear Father in heaven, we are so happy you have adopted us into your family. There is a great sense of peace that comes from knowing where and to whom we belong. We thank you for that peace. Today, as we continue working through this workbook, we ask you to neither leave us where we are nor as we are. We ask you to help us draw near to you so we may each become the person you intended us to be all along. We want to be true members of your family, Lord. Show us the way. Amen.

### Meeting & Greeting

*If you are working through this workbook on your own rather than participating in a small group study, please skip to the section entitled, "Getting Started."*

Welcome to our eighth week in the *My Secret Loss* small group study.

As our icebreaker for this week, tell us about something that has annoyed you perhaps since childhood, such as a pet peeve. However, please do not mention anyone or anything related to our study group.

______________________________________________

______________________________________________

______________________________________________

## Getting Started

How does it make you feel to know that God has adopted you into his family and you are heirs to his kingdom?

______________________________________________

______________________________________________

______________________________________________

What are the benefits to you as a child of God?

______________________________________________

______________________________________________

______________________________________________

## Let It Go! A continuation of the author's story

*This section builds upon the author's initial story. If you are participating in a small group study, a volunteer is invited to read this piece aloud.*

What was wrong with me? I don't know where that anger, rage, and hatred came from during my ten-year class reunion. That classmate had nothing to do with my high school pregnancy and my ultimate choice. Why was I blaming him? I buried my newly discovered anger and hate as deeply as I could, trying to prevent it from surfacing ever again.

I don't remember being angry at the time of my abortion. Instead, I remember being afraid of being hurt. I remember being afraid of being ostracized by my family, my friends, and the community. I remember feeling desperate and alone.

Sometimes people fail. Sometimes they fail to recognize we need help. Sometimes they fail to support us. Sometimes they make choices to support themselves without regard to our needs. Sometimes we refuse their help. Sometimes we fail to help ourselves.

When I think about my teenage years, I can create a long list of people who may have failed me at times leading up to my unintended pregnancy and as I was making my decision to have an abortion. Many questions come to my mind: Why did I feel so alone in my home? Who was supposed to help me understand what a healthy dating relationship looked like? Why didn't my friends help me stay on a better path for my life? Why didn't the father of the baby love me? How could I have fallen for his lines? Where were the leaders in our church? How come the information I received about abortion was not accurate? Why did I fear the gossip of the community? Did anyone notice I was struggling? Where was God?

I remember my mother would try to approach me from time to time. She would come into my bedroom and ask if I was ok or if anything was wrong. I wouldn't talk to her. I made it clear I wanted to be left alone. I never allowed her to break through my personal barriers. I was convinced she was questioning me in order to find fault with whatever I was doing. I didn't want a lecture. I didn't want to hear any accusations.

Perhaps because I would rarely talk to my mother, she decided I should talk with one of the pastors in town. He was the pastor at a different church from ours. He was probably in his thirties or early forties, and he was recently divorced. I met with him at his house for a few weeks, until he approached me sexually. I never went back.

I often have wondered why my friends didn't talk to me about improving the path I was on. Perhaps they didn't know what to say. I think one friend chose to protect herself, from what exactly I do not know. She sent me a poem, handwritten on lined notebook paper. She had burned the edges of the paper. The poem's message was that she didn't want to be my friend anymore, but she never explained why. I tried to find out what she was really trying to say, but she wouldn't take my calls. In time, I let it drop and I lost a friend. Friends often fail each other by what they say and do and by what they don't say or do.

Did everyone fail? Probably not. But the failures of others and our own failures can hurt and anger us. We live in an imperfect world.

Our own failures and the failures of others can hurt us. I should have sought advice from someone about healthy relationships. With the right advice, maybe I would have changed course before getting pregnant. After discovering I was pregnant, I should have sought solid counsel about my options rather than try to solve the problem on my own.

Instead, I never talked to anyone about my pregnancy to see if there was someone who could help me in ways other than abortion. I didn't want to face my mother's reaction. I didn't trust the church leaders or others in authority. I was afraid of losing my friends.

I didn't talk to the father either. I believed he would somehow blame me for becoming pregnant. I was afraid of his potential anger or rejection. How could I trust someone with my heart and body that I did not trust enough to take care of me if I became pregnant? Disappointment and embarrassment regarding my own lack of judgment swelled inside of me. It seemed less risky and painful to reject him without telling him about the pregnancy.

Although I believe I would have reached a different answer had I sought more advice about my options regarding this pregnancy, I may have received false, worldly advice: "Abortion is the best solution." I know of women who turned to their parents, others in the community, friends, or the father of the baby in their time of need and received the same advice. I didn't seek the advice of anyone. If I had, perhaps I would have made a different choice.

Finally, I didn't know God was just a prayer away. When I tried to pray for his help, I usually promised that if he would bail me out of trouble this one time, I would never do *it* again (whatever *it* was). I didn't recognize his answers to my prayers, so I just continued to do what I wanted. Looking back, I don't recall following through on any of my promises to him. Why didn't he make things more obvious to me? Isn't he all powerful? He could have prevented this situation. He could have solved it. Where was God?

After the abortion, I buried all of my feelings about the abortion and the perceived failures of everyone around me. The only way to start over was to clear every slate. Feelings were never resolved. They were just buried. Like rocks in a farmer's field, however, buried feelings work their way to the surface sooner or later. Unlike rocks in the field, the feelings surface with intensity because they were never managed properly in the first instance. Over the years, my once buried fears transformed themselves into anger, mistrust, and blame. They surfaced ten years later with intensity.

Fear didn't help me at the time of my unintended pregnancy, but burying my fears deep within my heart for years didn't help me move forward with an understanding heart. My fears surfaced as blame and anger. Upon realizing this truth, I began to identify those whom I blamed. Ultimately, I had to forgive them. It was the only way to let it go.

> *Get rid of all bitterness, rage and anger, brawling and slander, along with every form of malice. Be kind and compassionate to one another, forgiving each other, just as in Christ God forgave you.* Ephesians 4:31-32

## Forgiving Others and Forgiving Yourself

In what ways might the author's friends, family, and community have failed her? What could they have done differently?

____________________________________________

____________________________________________

____________________________________________

In what ways did the author probably fail herself? What could she have done differently?

____________________________________________

____________________________________________

____________________________________________

Can you think of other ways friends, family, and community might fail a woman, causing her to choose abortion in one of her greatest times of need?

______________________________________________________

______________________________________________________

______________________________________________________

Can you think of ways that friends, family, or people in a community might fail a post-abortive woman as she begins to deal with her feelings of regret, guilt, shame, and grief?

______________________________________________________

______________________________________________________

______________________________________________________

Can you effectively get rid of anger against another person by ignoring your feelings or by driving your feelings deep beneath the surface? Why or why not?

______________________________________________________

______________________________________________________

______________________________________________________

> *For if you forgive men when they sin against you, your heavenly Father will also forgive you. But if you do not forgive men their sins, your Father will not forgive your sins.*
> Matthew 6:14-15

## Bible Study

Forgiving others is a critical part of receiving forgiveness. Together, read aloud the words from Mark 11, verse 25.

> *And when you stand praying, if you hold anything against*

*anyone, forgive him, so that your Father in heaven may forgive you your sins.*

What does it mean to forgive someone?

___

___

___

Max Lucado, a prolific Christian author and pastor, once described resentment as a prison, and he then "pointed out that when we put someone in our jail cell of hatred, we are stuck guarding the door."[15] In order to hold someone in prison for his deeds, you have to guard the door. As a result, neither of you can leave the prison. How does forgiving others provide freedom for you?

___

___

___

For some of us, the failures of others in our lives are never-ending. They repeat their behaviors over and over and over. This is common in the case of abusive relationships. Please read Matthew 18:21-35.

*Then Peter came to Jesus and asked, "Lord, how many times shall I forgive my brother when he sins against me? Up to seven times?"*

*Jesus answered, "I tell you, not seven times, but seventy-seven times.*

*"Therefore, the kingdom of heaven is like a king who wanted to settle accounts with his servants. As he began the settlement, a man who owed him ten thousand talents was brought to him. Since he was not able to pay, the master*

15 Max Lucado, *The Great House of God* (Nashville, TN: W Publishing Group, a Division of Thomas Nelson, Inc., 1997), 110.

*ordered that he and his wife and his children and all that he had be sold to repay the debt.*

*"The servant fell on his knees before him. 'Be patient with me,' he begged, 'and I will pay back everything.' The servant's master took pity on him, canceled the debt and let him go.*

*"But when that servant went out, he found one of his fellow servants who owed him a hundred denarii. He grabbed him and began to choke him. 'Pay back what you owe me!' he demanded.*

*"His fellow servant fell to his knees and begged him, 'Be patient with me, and I will pay you back.'*

*"But he refused. Instead, he went off and had the man thrown into prison until he could pay the debt. When the other servants saw what had happened, they were greatly distressed and went and told their master everything that had happened.*

*"Then the master called the servant in. 'You wicked servant,' he said, 'I canceled all that debt of yours because you begged me to. Shouldn't you have had mercy on your fellow servant just as I had on you?' In anger his master turned him over to the jailers to be tortured, until he should pay back all he owed.*

*"This is how my heavenly Father will treat each of you unless you forgive your brother from your heart."*

Some Bible translations say that we are to forgive our brother seventy times seven (490) times. Does this mean we should keep a record so we know when the right number has been met? Explain.

______________________________________________

______________________________________________

______________________________________________

Considering this parable, assume God is the king and you are the first servant. How are we supposed to show our appreciation for the forgiveness we have received from God?

______________________________

______________________________

______________________________

There are some people who don't know how they have hurt us. Others believe they have helped us, when they have not. Others don't care what they may have done to us. There are some who continue to hurt us by never changing their ways. Is it harder to forgive people like these? Why?

______________________________

______________________________

______________________________

Does forgiveness mean we need to make ourselves vulnerable to someone's hurtful ways over and over? Explain.

______________________________

______________________________

______________________________

Please read Colossians 3:12-14.

> *Therefore, as God's chosen people, holy and dearly loved, clothe yourselves with compassion, kindness, humility, gentleness and patience. Bear with each other and forgive whatever grievances you may have against one another. Forgive as the Lord forgave you. And over all these virtues put on love, which binds them all together in perfect unity.*

Here we are encouraged to use compassion, kindness, humility, gentleness, and patience. How will these traits make it easier to forgive those who have hurt or angered us?

______________________________________________

______________________________________________

______________________________________________

Is it necessary to tell people we forgive them, or can we simply forgive them in our hearts? Explain your thoughts.

______________________________________________

______________________________________________

______________________________________________

## Reflection & Encouragement

> *To forgive for the moment is not difficult. But to go on forgiving, to forgive the same offense every time it recurs to the memory – there's the real tussle.* – C. S. Lewis[16]

> *When you harbor bitterness, happiness will dock elsewhere.* – Anonymous[17]

## Memory Verse

> *See to it that no one misses the grace of God and that no bitter root grows up to cause trouble and defile many.*
> Hebrews 12:15

## Closing Prayer

Lord God, heavenly Father, we thank you for your everlasting

16 C. S. Lewis, *Letters to Malcolm: Chiefly on Prayer* (New York: Harcourt, Inc., 1964), 27.

17 'Wetzell and Freeman, *God's Survival Guide For Women*, 30.

love. Through Jesus, we know we have been forgiven for our sins. We want to show others your love by forgiving them for the ways they have wronged us. Sometimes this is hard for us to do, especially in regard to those who have not sought our forgiveness or continue to hurt us. We pray that you will soften our hearts and remove all bitterness so we may forgive them as well. We pray in Jesus' name. Amen.

## Homework

- Place copies of the memory verse in convenient locations in your home and place of employment. Read it several times each day until you have committed it to memory.
- If you are participating in a small group study, read through Week 9 of the workbook to prepare for next week's meeting.
- In your journal, list all those whom you believe may have failed you before you discovered you were pregnant and when you chose to have an abortion. Note how their failures may have impacted your behavior which led to your unintended pregnancy. In each case, consider what you could have done differently to have positively impacted the situation. Forgive them in your prayers.
- Do not approach any of the people in your list at this time to tell them you forgive them, unless it is a mutually known thorn in your relationship. Even then, approach them only after prayer, seeking God's timing and guidance.

Week 9

# How Do I Make It Right?

*For God so loved the world that he gave his one and only Son, that whoever believes in him shall not perish but have eternal life.* John 3:16

## Opening Prayer

Our Father, we cannot thank you enough for your love, grace, and mercy – all of which have no end. Through Jesus' death on the cross and resurrection, you have bridged the gap between your holiness and our sinful lives. We welcome your presence into our lives and ask you to continue your good works within us. Teach us to live according to your plans. Enable us to know the joy and peace that comes only from a life with you. Thank you, dear Father. Amen.

## Meeting & Greeting

*If you are working through this workbook on your own rather than participating in a small group study, please skip to the section entitled, "Getting Started."*

Welcome to our ninth week in this *My Secret Loss* small group study. Thank you for continuing to support each other now as sisters in Christ, as we continue to seek life after abortion.

As you greet each other this week, please tell us about a time you wanted to "create a new you," either through a new outfit, hairstyle, job, diet, or similar change. What did you do and how did it turn out?

______________________________

______________________________

______________________________

## Getting Started

Some situations are "old wounds." Bringing up "old wounds" to someone who is not aware of the wound or does not realize they may have caused the wound can often cause more harm than good. List reasons why bringing up "old wounds" might be wise; list reasons why bringing up "old wounds" might be unwise.

______________________________

______________________________

______________________________

Let's pray together right now, asking God to help us know if and when the time is right to bring up "old wounds" in an effort to make peace in a relationship:

> Father God, you know we have been hurt by the people in our lives, both by their actions and their inactions. It is easier to forgive them if we can talk to them about our pain; however, we recognize it is not always best to bring up "old wounds." Help us to discern if and when a discussion will be helpful or hurtful. Do not allow us to mention past pain and long-felt wounds if by doing so we will cause more harm. Thank you for your guiding hand. Remove from our hearts all bitterness and enable all of our conversations to reflect your love. We pray in Jesus' name. Amen.

## How Do I Make It Right? A continuation of the author's story

*Again, this section builds upon the author's initial story. If you are participating in a small group study, a volunteer is invited to read this piece aloud.*

One day, my daughters came home from a church youth group meeting armed with many pro-life pamphlets and brochures. They showed them to me. They told me they didn't understand how someone could ever choose abortion. Their tone made it clear they felt disdain for someone who could be so heartless.

I tried to tell them I agreed that abortion was wrong, but noted they did not understand everything that might drive a young woman to make that choice. I told them some girls discover they are pregnant and have no one to help them. They become desperate. I told them some young girls are taken to the abortion clinic by well-meaning parents or friends who believe in their hearts abortion is the best answer. I told them some women are forced into abortion by a boyfriend or husband who demands cooperation, perhaps because they don't believe they can take on the responsibility of a child. I told them some couples face devastating news that to continue with a pregnancy could be critically harmful to the baby and mother alike, and they believe in their hearts abortion is the best solution. Finally, after explaining that I agreed abortion is the wrong choice, I asked our daughters to have compassion for women who have had abortions. I told them these women will forever live with the consequences of their choice.

I didn't tell them I was one of these women.

I thought about telling our daughters about my choice, but I couldn't do it. *What if they couldn't or wouldn't understand? How would they handle the thought that their mother made the same choice they were so adamantly against? What if they considered me with the same disdain I had just heard in their voices? What if they could not or would not forgive me?* I was afraid the knowledge of my choice would damage our relationships forever. Again, hiding my choice was the only answer for me at that time.

Yet I felt hypocritical for not telling them. I was afraid they would someday interpret my silence as a lie, making it difficult if not impossible to believe or trust anything else I have said or will say as their mother. I was afraid they would lose their trust in me if I didn't tell them the truth.

After months of contemplation and prayer, I began to write about my past choices. Writing became an incredible avenue for reflection. After I had finished an initial draft telling the story of my past choices, a unique window of opportunity opened for a conversation with our oldest daughter. I was going to Houston and she was going to meet me there. We were going to spend a long weekend together, just the two of us. So I gave her my story to read while she was on the plane, knowing that while we were in Houston, she and I could talk about it for a long time if needed.

I was extremely nervous when I met her at the airport; I could think of nothing else. I tried to observe her every move, hoping to determine if she read the book and how she felt about me now that she knew this piece of my past.

She didn't say anything about it at first; but when we got into the car, she started to talk.

"Mom," she said softly. "I read your book."

My heart raced in fear of what she might say next. My hands began to shake. I feared the worst. I feared she would not understand. I prayed quickly and silently, one word, *Help.*

"I had to keep putting it down because it made me cry. Mom?" she prodded.

"What honey?" I asked as I tentatively turned to look at her.

"I still love you," she said. "You're not the same person you were back then. God changes people."

*God loves you just the way you are, but he refuses to leave you that way. He wants you to be just like Jesus.*
– Max Lucado[18]

With abortion, there is no one to tell that you are sorry. There is no way to bring the baby back, to apologize to the baby, or to make it right. Once done, it is done. There is no direct reconciliation with the baby.

Every time I think of our daughter's words, my heart cries with thankfulness. Through her love and understanding, I know in my heart as well as in my head that I am forgiven. Through her words, I knew I had found reconciliation first with God through Christ and then with my lost baby.

*Yet, O Lord, you are our Father.*
*We are the clay, you are the potter;*
*we are all the work of your hand.*
Isaiah 64:8

## Finding Reconciliation

Reconciliation between people is generally the act of restoring harmony or resolving differences.[19] List examples of when reconciliation between two people might be needed.

________________________________________

________________________________________

________________________________________

With whom might a woman who has had an abortion want to reconcile?

________________________________________

________________________________________

________________________________________

18 Max Lucado, *Just Like Jesus; with teen story adaptations by Monica Hall* (Nashville, TN: Tommy Nelson ®, a Division of Thomas Nelson, Inc., 2003), 11.

19 *Merriam-Webster's Collegiate Dictionary*, 11th ed., s.v. "reconciliation."

When two people are in conflict, having an argument, or are angry with each other, what is the most common means to begin reconciliation?

___

___

___

It is easiest to reach reconciliation with another when both parties are willing to discuss what happened until mutual understanding is reached. What can you do when the other person will not talk about it?

___

___

___

Is reconciliation with all people possible? If you are unable to reach reconciliation with someone, how could you reach closure for your own heart?

___

___

___

The author found reconciliation with her lost baby through the acceptance and understanding of her living daughters. Try to list a number of ways to reach a symbolic reconciliation with our babies lost through abortion.

___

___

___

## Bible Study

Consider reading aloud verses 19-23a from Colossians, chapter 1.

> *For God was pleased to have all his fullness dwell in him, and through him to reconcile to himself all things, whether things on earth or things in heaven, by making peace through his blood, shed on the cross. Once you were alienated from God and were enemies in your minds because of your evil behavior. But now he has reconciled you by Christ's physical body through death to present you holy in his sight, without blemish and free from accusation – if you continue in your faith, established and firm, not moved from the hope held out in the gospel.*

Reconciliation with God is a change in the relationship between God and man based on the changed status of man through the redemptive work of Christ.[20] How do we know God wants us to be reconciled with him?

______________________________________________

______________________________________________

______________________________________________

How does God see us once we are reconciled to him in Christ?

______________________________________________

______________________________________________

______________________________________________

> *For it is by grace you have been saved, through faith – and this not from yourselves, it is the gift of God – not by works, so that no one can boast. Ephesians 2:8-9*

Please read the following passage from 2 Corinthians 5:17-19.

20 J. D. Douglas, ed., "Reconciliation." *New International Bible Dictionary* (Grand Rapids, MI: Zondervan, 1987).

*Therefore, if anyone is in Christ, he is a new creation; the old has gone, the new has come! All this is from God, who reconciled us to himself through Christ and gave us the ministry of reconciliation: that God was reconciling the world to himself in Christ, not counting men's sins against them. And he has committed to us the message of reconciliation.*

What do you think it means when it is said that "the old has gone, the new has come?"

________________________________________

________________________________________

________________________________________

What do you think might change in us when we are reconciled with God?

________________________________________

________________________________________

________________________________________

The apostle Paul speaks of several changes in us once we are reconciled to God. Read about renewed life in Ephesians 2:1-5 and 5:8-10 and Galatians 5:22, printed below, respectively.

*As for you, you were dead in your transgressions and sins, in which you used to live when you followed the ways of this world and of the ruler of the kingdom of the air, the spirit who is now at work in those who are disobedient. All of us also lived among them at one time, gratifying the cravings of our sinful nature and following its desires and thoughts. Like the rest, we were by nature objects of wrath. But because of his great love for us, God, who is rich in mercy, made us alive with Christ even when we were dead in transgressions – it is by grace you have been saved.*

*For you were once darkness, but now you are light in the Lord. Live as children of light (for the fruit of the light*

> *consists in all goodness, righteousness and truth) and find out what pleases the Lord.*
>
> *But the fruit of the Spirit is love, joy, peace, patience, kindness, goodness, faithfulness, gentleness and self-control. Against such things there is no law.*

There are many things in the world that may look fun or exciting to some of us, such as gambling, drunkenness, drugs, and other forms of living on the edge. For those who like to live life on the edge, what do you think they are seeking?

______________________________________________

______________________________________________

______________________________________________

When someone lives life on the edge, what are the risks they are taking? What potential downfalls do they face?

______________________________________________

______________________________________________

______________________________________________

What does a life in Christ give us?

______________________________________________

______________________________________________

______________________________________________

> *This is love for God: to obey his commands. And his commands are not burdensome, for everyone born of God overcomes the world. This is the victory that has overcome the world, even our faith. Who is it that overcomes the world? Only he who believes that Jesus is the Son of God.*
> 1 John 5:3-5

We have talked about reconciliation with God, others, and with our lost babies. Although we are unable to directly reach reconciliation with our lost babies today, such will be possible in heaven. Read Isaiah 65:17.

> *"Behold, I will create*
> *new heavens and a new earth.*
> *The former things will not be remembered,*
> *nor will they come to mind."*

Through God's grace, we will meet our lost babies in heaven. What feelings come to your heart as you consider this truth?

______________________________________________

______________________________________________

______________________________________________

Through reconciliation with God, righteousness will be restored within us. Our sins will be wiped clean. Will we need to worry about facing our lost babies in heaven? Why or why not?

______________________________________________

______________________________________________

______________________________________________

> *I waited patiently for the Lord;*
> *he turned to me and heard my cry.*
> *He lifted me out of the slimy pit,*
> *out of the mud and mire;*
> *he set my feet on a rock*
> *and gave me a firm place to stand.*
> *He put a new song in my mouth,*
> *a hymn of praise to our God.*
> *Many will see and fear*
> *and put their trust in the Lord.*
> Psalm 40:1-3

## Reflection & Encouragement

*Mistakes offer the possibility for redemption and a new start in God's kingdom. No matter what you're guilty of, God can restore your innocence.* – Barbara Johnson[21]

*With God, it isn't who you were that matters; it's who you are becoming.* – Liz Curtis Higgs[22]

## Memory Verse

*The Lord is my shepherd, I shall not want.*
*He makes me lie down in green pastures,*
*he leads me beside quiet waters,*
*he restores my soul.*
*He guides me in paths of righteousness*
*for his name's sake.*
Psalm 23:1-3

## Closing Prayer

Dear Father in heaven, we thank you for enabling us to be near you through your Son, Jesus Christ. Your endless love never ceases to amaze us as we look upon our lives and the ways we have failed you and failed the people in our lives. Bless the hearts of those we have hurt through our choices, enabling them to give us the gift of their forgiveness just as you have forgiven us. We seek reconciliation with them and with our lost children. Only through your love and grace can we be sure such reconciliation is possible. Above all, however, we thank you for reconciling us to you. Amen.

21 Wetzell and Freeman, *God's Survival Guide For Women*, 120.
22 Wetzell and Freeman, *God's Survival Guide For Women*, 134.

## Homework

- Place copies of the memory verse in convenient locations in your home and place of employment. Read it several times each day until you have committed it to memory.
- If you are participating in a small group study, please read through Week 10 of the workbook to prepare for next week's meeting.
- Write a letter of confession and apology in your journal or notebook to your lost baby or babies. You may want to describe some of the significant losses you believe he or she has faced as a result of your decision. Close by asking for his or her forgiveness.
- List in your journal or notebook your feelings about meeting your lost child in heaven. What are your fears? What joys do you hope to embrace?

## Week 10

# It's Not an Independent Path

*What a man desires is unfailing love.* Proverbs 19:22

## Opening Prayer

Our Father, we thank you for enabling us to know you and your love for us. We thank you for never failing us even though we have failed you and others. Today, dear Father, strengthen your love in our hearts by enabling us to show your love to those around us. Be with us today, tomorrow, and forever. Amen.

## Meeting & Greeting

> *If you are working through this workbook on your own rather than participating in a small group study, please skip to the section entitled, "Getting Started."*

Welcome to our tenth and final week in this *My Secret Loss* small group study. Last week we learned that we are reconciled with God through Christ Jesus. A great way to feel God's love is by sharing his love with each other. Thank you for continuing to support each other again this week in this group.

This week, please tell us about a funny story involving you and a childhood friend.

---

______________________________________________

______________________________________________

## Getting Started

Why should we not be afraid of meeting our babies in heaven?

______________________________________________

______________________________________________

______________________________________________

## No Longer Alone: A continuation of the author's story

*Again, this section builds upon the author's initial story. If you are participating in a small group study, a volunteer is invited to read this piece aloud.*

I was told my sister went to heaven. I never saw her again. When Mom talked about her, she would be very sad. Then Daddy went to heaven. I knew I'd never see him again. Mom seemed to be worried about how she would manage our house and family business alone. Daddy couldn't come home to help her. Heaven must be very far away because when people go there, they never come back, not for any reason and no matter how much we miss them or need them. You never see them again. In Sunday school, I learned that God is in heaven too. So he must be very far away, too.

That was the way my nine-year-old mind understood death, heaven, and the existence of God.

Although my parents took me to church throughout my childhood and teenage years, that's all I understood about God. He was very far away. While I believed he existed, I thought he was not really involved in the day-to-day world here on earth. The Bible was like a history book to me, designed to tell us about what God was like back in the days when he spent more time here on Earth.

Over the years, as time passed (time that seemed to go hand-in-hand with my reluctant discovery that terminating my pregnancy ended the life of my baby), I began to discover that God was closer than I thought. He put people in my life to help me get to know him. My husband was the first to learn of my earlier, regrettable choices. He showed me what forgiveness and acceptance can look like. My children helped me discover the 1 Corinthians 13 kind of love. Friends lived their faith in loving appreciation to God, a God they seemed to believe was here, living in their day-to-day world. Finally, my sister invited me to a women's retreat sponsored by her church. There, I first discovered just how near God really was and is today.

I went to the retreat with my sister simply because she invited me. I wasn't terribly excited about it. There were worship times and seminar times and worship times and seminar times and more worship times. I was more of a "worship-once-a-week-whether-I needed-to-or-not" kind of person, so spending a whole weekend in worship and study seemed a little overwhelming and exhausting to me. But on Saturday night, my life was changed forever.

Something was different that night. I discovered that God is real, he is here, and he has been just a prayer away at all times. I prayed during worship, admitting my sins and asking Jesus to be my Savior. Suddenly, in an all-powerful, only-a-God-kind-of-way, I could feel a physical fullness in my chest. It almost felt like a struggle over who was going to get to keep the space encompassed by my rib cage, the old me or the Spirit of God. I found myself praying that God would take me, keep me, and live in me. I prayed that I would let go of my old self and let God have all of me, not really knowing what that prayer might mean for me then or in the future. And so he took over, and I let go.

Now I know God is here today in the day-to-day. He has shown me his presence in so many ways, big and small. He has lifted fog so I could drive safely home in the dark, given me peace in the middle of a traffic jam in downtown Dallas, and caused the phone to ring when I longingly needed a friend. He has shown his love, grace, and mercy through his forgiveness, his continual prodding of me, and his daily answers to my prayers.

Until I truly knew of God's presence, I had an extraordinarily strong need for acceptance from my friends, my co-workers, my boss, and others. I needed their approval. I sought their approval through many means, whether it was through attempted work perfection, effort bordering that of a workaholic, generosity, or whatever else I perceived would meet with their approval.

Now, instead, I know that God really was, is, and always will be very close. I am secure in God's love. In that security, I can be true to him first and foremost. I can also be true to myself and my family, and I can be confident in my relationships with others. I can focus on God's will for my life, knowing that all things will work out for good in the end. Although I still enjoy and need the love and support of the people closest to me, I can seek and embrace their love in a healthy manner.

My path is no longer an independent path. I know I'll never be alone again. I live life with Christ as my foundation, and he will never leave me.

He wants to be your foundation for life too.

> *Therefore everyone who hears these words of mine and puts them into practice is like a wise man who built his house on the rock. The rains came down, the streams rose, and the winds blew and beat against that house; yet it did not fall, because it had its foundation on the rock.*
> – Jesus, Matthew 7:24-25

## He Is My Foundation

Compare and contrast the author's confidence in her relationships before she had a personal relationship with Christ and after she had a personal relationship with Christ.

How do you think her life changed when she discovered God was not in a faraway heaven?

______________________________________________

______________________________________________

______________________________________________

The author now believes God is here with each of us in the day-to-day. What signs have you seen that would indicate God is with us every day?

______________________________________________

______________________________________________

______________________________________________

## Bible Study

Let's begin with John 14:23.

> *Jesus replied, "If anyone loves me, he will obey my teaching. My Father will love him, and we will come to him and make our home with him.*

According to this verse, God will make his home with us. What do you think this means for your daily life?

______________________________________________

______________________________________________

______________________________________________

Consider reading aloud Matthew 28:18-20.

> *Then Jesus came to them and said, "All authority in heaven and on earth has been given to me. Therefore go and make disciples of all nations, baptizing them in the name of the Father and of the Son and of the Holy Spirit, and teaching them to obey everything I have commanded you. And surely I am with you always, to the very end of the age.*

Will God ever abandon us?

___

___

___

When a tragedy strikes in our lives (such as a death, illness, or accident), sometimes it seems like God has abandoned us. God never promised that life would be easy. How does God help us through difficult times?

___

___

___

What can we do to draw God near to us during difficult times?

___

___

___

God put many people in the author's life to support her and to show her his love. Read Romans 12:6-8, printed below.

> *We have different gifts, according to the grace given us. If a man's gift is prophesying, let him use it in proportion to his faith. If it is serving, let him serve; if it is teaching, let him teach; if it is encouraging, let him encourage; if it is contributing to the needs of others, let him give generously; if it is leadership, let him govern diligently; if it is showing mercy, let him do it cheerfully.*

How does God use the gifts and talents of people to draw others to him?

___

___

___

Consider these many talents and discuss the ways each of us can support others who have had abortions and now struggle with their decisions.

______________________________________________

______________________________________________

______________________________________________

How will supporting others who have had abortions help us heal from our own wounds?

______________________________________________

______________________________________________

______________________________________________

Please read 1 Peter 4:8-11.

> *Above all, love each other deeply, because love covers over a multitude of sins. Offer hospitality to one another without grumbling. Each one should use whatever gift he has received to serve others, faithfully administering God's grace in its various forms. If anyone speaks, he should do it as one speaking the very words of God. If anyone serves, he should do it with the strength God provides, so that in all things God may be praised through Jesus Christ. To him be the glory and the power for ever and ever. Amen*

Someone once described a very special friend as being like God with skin. What do you think that could mean?

______________________________________________

______________________________________________

______________________________________________

Please share a story about a friend, sister, or family member who did something for you that was so kind, helpful, or loving that you could describe the action as one brought by God?

______________________________________________

Do all "God with skin" actions have to be big, important, or unique activities? Explain.

Please read Romans 12:9-16, below.

> *Love must be sincere. Hate what is evil; cling to what is good. Be devoted to one another in brotherly love. Honor one another above yourselves. Never be lacking in zeal, but keep your spiritual fervor, serving the Lord. Be joyful in hope, patient in affliction, faithful in prayer. Share with God's people who are in need. Practice hospitality.*
>
> *Bless those who persecute you; bless and do not curse. Rejoice with those who rejoice; mourn with those who mourn. Live in harmony with one another. Do not be proud, but be willing to associate with people of low position. Do not be conceited.*

By helping others, what might they learn about God's love?

Some of us are not able to obtain help or support from our friends and family members. Please share with each other the names of groups, organizations, or professional services you have worked with, talked to, or are otherwise familiar that offer services in your area for post-abortive women.

When we feel we have been blessed by God's love and forgiveness, whether through this workbook and study or through another means, we are often very excited and have a strong desire to share God's blessings with others. How do we discern when the people around us are ready to know more about God's love and forgiveness?

Why is it important to avoid going too far or too fast for someone who is hurting, even when pursued with the best of intentions?

*Perfume and incense bring joy to the heart;*
*And the pleasantness of one's friend springs from his earnest counsel.* Proverbs 27:9

## Reflection & Encouragement

*Let God love you through others and let God love others through you.* – D. M. Street[23]

## Memory Verse

*A generous man will prosper; he who refreshes others will himself be refreshed.* Proverbs 11:25

23 Caron Loveless, *Hugs from Heaven: Embraced by the Savior* (West Monroe, LA: Howard Publishing Co., Inc., 1998), 101.

## A Time of Thanksgiving & Praise

For those participating in a small group study, take a few minutes to wish each other well as we close this study. Although formal sessions for this group have been completed, we encourage each of you to continue to support and encourage each other as may be needed or desired. If there is a way the group or any of its members can minister to you, please ask.

## Closing Prayer

> Father, your presence each day brings joy and new possibilities. You enable us to cope with our fears, disappointments, and our feelings of inadequacy. We are your children, and we know you will care for us according to our every need. Sometimes your caring nature is made evident through the people in our lives. Thank you for the loving and faithful family and friends you've given us. Bless us today with hearts of love and service so we too might draw others closer to you. Open our eyes to the opportunities in our lives in which we may show your love. In Jesus' name we pray. Amen.

## Homework

- Place copies of the memory verse in convenient locations in your home and place of employment. Read it several times each day until you have committed it to memory.
- Make a list of concerns or worries that remain unresolved. Identify resources that may help you with these unresolved concerns. Consider resources listed in this workbook, discussed in the small group, and available through your church library, a nearby pregnancy center, your pastor, a Christian counselor, and your friends or family members. There are many people who are willing and capable of helping you take the next step in your healing process.

Appendix A

# Additional Resources

## Recommended Reading:

Randy Alcorn, *Why Pro-Life* (Sisters, OR: Multnomah Publishers, Inc., 2004).

Jim Anderson, *The Heart of a Woman: Daughters, Flower, Princess* (Memrah, 1998).

Sandra Picklesimer Aldrich, "Choices for Life," *Daily Devotions 1993* (Nashville TN: Thomas Nelson, Inc., 1993).

Linda Cochran, *Forgiven and Set Free* (Grand Rapids, MI: Baker Books, 1996).

Luci Freed and Penny Yvonne Salazar, *A Season to Heal* (Nashville, TN: Cumberland House Publishing, Inc., 1993).

Jack W. Hayford, *I'll Hold You in Heaven* (Ventura CA: Regal Books, 1990).

Sydna Massé and Joan Phillips, *Her Choice to Heal* (Colorado Springs, CO: Life

Journey®, imprint of Cook Communications Ministries, 2004).

Frank E. Perretti, *Tilly* (Wheaton IL: Crossway Books, 2003).

## Internet Resources:

Elizabeth Ministry International is an international movement designed to support women and their families during the joys, trials, and sorrows of the childbearing years. Elizabeth Ministry's mission is to cherish children, encourage families, and build community. They offer peer support, mentoring, spiritual nourishment, and educational and inspirational resources. *www.elizabethministry.com*

The Elliott Institute is a national nonprofit organization dedicated to research, education, and outreach regarding the effects of abortion on women, men, families, and society. *www.afterabortion.org*

Ramah International, a nonprofit ministry whose mission is to assist those hurting from post-abortion syndrome, raises the level of awareness about post-abortion syndrome and the needs of individuals who have experienced abortion and provides post-abortion syndrome resources, research, and training programs necessary to mobilize and equip "the church" to reach out and help those affected by abortion. *www.ramahinternational.org*

Project Rachel is the name of the Catholic Church's healing ministry to those who have been involved in abortion. It operates as a network of professional counselors and priests, all trained to provide one-on-one spiritual and psychological care for those who are suffering because of an abortion. *www.hopeafterabortion.com*

# Appendix B

# Sample Group Covenant

## Purpose & value terms of your small group covenant

Please take a moment to read the sample group covenant below. You might want to use it as a basis for your own small group covenant, though your group is *your* group so feel free to adapt it as you wish.

## Group Covenant

**Unconditional Love** – I covenant that there is nothing my fellow group members have done or will do that will make me stop loving them. I may not agree with their actions, but I vow to love them as persons created in the image of God and do all I can to hold them up to God's affirming love.

**Confidentiality** – I covenant to respect the privacy of all members of this small group and will keep all information shared by others within this group. I will not discuss another member's words, attitudes, or life conditions with anyone outside the group.

**Honesty** – I covenant to be honest with other members of the group. This includes sharing my own impressions and opinions in a loving, constructive spirit, not a hateful, destructive one. We remain sisters in Christ even when our personalities don't always fit perfectly and when our preferences differ.

**Respect** – I covenant to respect the thoughts, feelings, opinions, and experiences of all members of the group even when they are different from my own. I will not "badger," stand in judgment, belittle, or in any other way invalidate another member of the group and will lovingly confront others when I perceive they are doing so. Respect means I don't "jump in with advice" (unless someone specifically asks for it), try to "fix" someone, dominate group time, or talk to "hear myself talk."

**Prayer** – I covenant to pray for each member in the group in some regular fashion, believing that our caring heavenly Father wishes his children to pray for one another and ask him for the blessings they need.

**Accountability** – I covenant to come each week as prepared as possible. I will make a serious attempt to keep up with readings and homework assignments and to be working on a daily habit of prayer and meditation on God's Word. I will pray regularly for the others in my group.

**Openness** – I covenant to strive to become a more open person, disclosing my feelings, my struggles, my joys, and my hurts to those in my small group as much as I am able. The degree to which I do so implies that I cannot make it without them, that I trust them with my problems and my dreams, and that I need them. This is to affirm their worth to me as a person.

**Sensitivity** – I covenant to be sensitive to all members of our group as together we strive to know and understand each other. I will be attentive when they are speaking and protect their feelings even though they react differently than me. I will not be shocked, condemning, or condescending. I will not resort to labels such as "emotional," "not very bright," "too intellectual," "liberal," or "conservative."

**Availability** – I covenant that anything I have – time, energy, insight, possessions- is at the disposal of those in my small group who need it – to the limit of my resources. I give these freely as I give myself as long as they do not interfere with the prior covenants with God or my family which take precedence.

My vow – With the good Lord as my helper, I enter into this covenant,

signed: ____________________________________________

## Small Group Administrative Matters

Some or all of the following items should be announced or determined as a group during your first meeting. You may think of other similar administrative matters that are relevant to your group.

When and where will the group meet?

______________________________

______________________________

______________________________

How often will the group meet?

______________________________

______________________________

______________________________

For how long will each meeting last? (Each week's material anticipates your meetings will last about ninety minutes.)

______________________________

______________________________

______________________________

Will the refreshments be served: before, during, or after the meeting? Are there any special dietary issues to remember, such as no caffeine or no sugar?

______________________________

______________________________

______________________________

Is phone and/or e-mail an acceptable means of communicating for all members?

______________________________

________________________________________________

________________________________________________

Who will follow up with members who miss a meeting (in addition to the small group leader)?

________________________________________________

________________________________________________

________________________________________________

Check the calendar. Are any regularly scheduled dates or times not going to work for a significant number of the group members?

________________________________________________

________________________________________________

________________________________________________

What happens if the small group leader is unable to attend due to illness or emergency?

________________________________________________

________________________________________________

________________________________________________

What happens if weather or another emergency creates a need to cancel or reschedule a meeting?

________________________________________________

________________________________________________

________________________________________________

# Appendix C

# Memory Verses

The following pages have the memory verses from each chapter. The pages have been formatted for easy removal. Cut out the memory verse for each particular week. Place copies of it in easy to notice locations throughout your home, office, and car, enabling you to read it several times a day and commit it to memory.

## Week 1 Memory Verse

*Why are you downcast, O my soul?*
*Why so disturbed within me?*
*Put your hope in God,*
*for I will yet praise him,*
*my Savior and my God.*
Psalm 42:5


*Why are you downcast, O my soul?*
*Why so disturbed within me?*
*Put your hope in God,*
*for I will yet praise him,*
*my Savior and my God.*
Psalm 42:5

*Why are you downcast, O my soul?*
*Why so disturbed within me?*
*Put your hope in God,*
*for I will yet praise him,*
*my Savior and my God.*
Psalm 42:5

*Why are you downcast, O my soul?*
*Why so disturbed within me?*
*Put your hope in God,*
*for I will yet praise him,*
*my Savior and my God.*
Psalm 42:5

*Why are you downcast, O my soul?*
*Why so disturbed within me?*
*Put your hope in God,*
*for I will yet praise him,*
*my Savior and my God.*
Psalm 42:5

*Why are you downcast, O my soul?*
*Why so disturbed within me?*
*Put your hope in God,*
*for I will yet praise him,*
*my Savior and my God.*
Psalm 42:5

## Week 2 Memory Verse

| | |
|---|---|
| *The Lord is close to the brokenhearted and saves those who are crushed in spirit.* Psalm 34:18 | *The Lord is close to the brokenhearted and saves those who are crushed in spirit.* Psalm 34:18 |
| *The Lord is close to the brokenhearted and saves those who are crushed in spirit.* Psalm 34:18 | *The Lord is close to the brokenhearted and saves those who are crushed in spirit.* Psalm 34:18 |
| *The Lord is close to the brokenhearted and saves those who are crushed in spirit.* Psalm 34:18 | *The Lord is close to the brokenhearted and saves those who are crushed in spirit.* Psalm 34:18 |

## Week 3 Memory Verse

| | |
|---|---|
| *If we confess our sins, he is faithful and just and will forgive us our sins and purify us from all unrighteousness.*<br>1 John 1:9 | *If we confess our sins, he is faithful and just and will forgive us our sins and purify us from all unrighteousness.*<br>1 John 1:9 |
| *If we confess our sins, he is faithful and just and will forgive us our sins and purify us from all unrighteousness.*<br>1 John 1:9 | *If we confess our sins, he is faithful and just and will forgive us our sins and purify us from all unrighteousness.*<br>1 John 1:9 |
| *If we confess our sins, he is faithful and just and will forgive us our sins and purify us from all unrighteousness.*<br>1 John 1:9 | *If we confess our sins, he is faithful and just and will forgive us our sins and purify us from all unrighteousness.*<br>1 John 1:9 |

## Week 4 Memory Verse

*But those who hope in*
*the Lord will renew their*
*strength.*
*They will soar on wings like*
*eagles; they will run and not*
*grow weary, they will walk*
*and not be faint.*
Isaiah 40:31

*But those who hope in*
*the Lord will renew their*
*strength.*
*They will soar on wings like*
*eagles; they will run and not*
*grow weary, they will walk*
*and not be faint.*
Isaiah 40:31

*But those who hope in*
*the Lord will renew their*
*strength.*
*They will soar on wings like*
*eagles; they will run and not*
*grow weary, they will walk*
*and not be faint.*
Isaiah 40:31

*But those who hope in*
*the Lord will renew their*
*strength.*
*They will soar on wings like*
*eagles; they will run and not*
*grow weary, they will walk*
*and not be faint.*
Isaiah 40:31

*But those who hope in*
*the Lord will renew their*
*strength.*
*They will soar on wings like*
*eagles; they will run and not*
*grow weary, they will walk*
*and not be faint.*
Isaiah 40:31

*But those who hope in*
*the Lord will renew their*
*strength.*
*They will soar on wings like*
*eagles; they will run and not*
*grow weary, they will walk*
*and not be faint.*
Isaiah 40:31

## Week 5 Memory Verse

*Trust in the Lord and do good; dwell in the land and enjoy safe pasture.*
*Delight yourself in the Lord and he will give you the desires of your heart.*
Psalm 37:3-4

*Trust in the Lord and do good; dwell in the land and enjoy safe pasture.*
*Delight yourself in the Lord and he will give you the desires of your heart.*
Psalm 37:3-4

*Trust in the Lord and do good; dwell in the land and enjoy safe pasture.*
*Delight yourself in the Lord and he will give you the desires of your heart.*
Psalm 37:3-4

*Trust in the Lord and do good; dwell in the land and enjoy safe pasture.*
*Delight yourself in the Lord and he will give you the desires of your heart.*
Psalm 37:3-4

*Trust in the Lord and do good; dwell in the land and enjoy safe pasture.*
*Delight yourself in the Lord and he will give you the desires of your heart.*
Psalm 37:3-4

*Trust in the Lord and do good; dwell in the land and enjoy safe pasture.*
*Delight yourself in the Lord and he will give you the desires of your heart.*
Psalm 37:3-4

## Week 6 Memory Verse

| | |
|---|---|
| *Though your sins are like scarlet, they shall be as white as snow; though they are red as crimson, they shall be like wool.* Isaiah 1:18 | *Though your sins are like scarlet, they shall be as white as snow; though they are red as crimson, they shall be like wool.* Isaiah 1:18 |
| *Though your sins are like scarlet, they shall be as white as snow; though they are red as crimson, they shall be like wool.* Isaiah 1:18 | *Though your sins are like scarlet, they shall be as white as snow; though they are red as crimson, they shall be like wool.* Isaiah 1:18 |
| *Though your sins are like scarlet, they shall be as white as snow; though they are red as crimson, they shall be like wool.* Isaiah 1:18 | *Though your sins are like scarlet, they shall be as white as snow; though they are red as crimson, they shall be like wool.* Isaiah 1:18 |

## Week 7 Memory Verse

*How great is the love the Father has lavished on us, that we should be called children of God! And that is what we are!* 1 John 3:1a

*How great is the love the Father has lavished on us, that we should be called children of God! And that is what we are!* 1 John 3:1a

*How great is the love the Father has lavished on us, that we should be called children of God! And that is what we are!* 1 John 3:1a

*How great is the love the Father has lavished on us, that we should be called children of God! And that is what we are!* 1 John 3:1a

*How great is the love the Father has lavished on us, that we should be called children of God! And that is what we are!* 1 John 3:1a

*How great is the love the Father has lavished on us, that we should be called children of God! And that is what we are!* 1 John 3:1a

## Week 8 Memory Verse

*See to it that no one misses the grace of God and that no bitter root grows up to cause trouble and defile many.*
Hebrews 12:15

*See to it that no one misses the grace of God and that no bitter root grows up to cause trouble and defile many.*
Hebrews 12:15

*See to it that no one misses the grace of God and that no bitter root grows up to cause trouble and defile many.*
Hebrews 12:15

*See to it that no one misses the grace of God and that no bitter root grows up to cause trouble and defile many.*
Hebrews 12:15

*See to it that no one misses the grace of God and that no bitter root grows up to cause trouble and defile many.*
Hebrews 12:15

*See to it that no one misses the grace of God and that no bitter root grows up to cause trouble and defile many.*
Hebrews 12:15

## Week 9 Memory Verse

*The Lord is my shepherd,*
*I shall not be in want.*
*He makes me lie down*
*in green pastures,*
*he leads me beside quiet waters,*
*he restores my soul.*
*He guides me*
*in paths of righteousness*
*for his name's sake.*
Psalm 23:1-3

*The Lord is my shepherd,*
*I shall not be in want.*
*He makes me lie down*
*in green pastures,*
*he leads me beside quiet waters,*
*he restores my soul.*
*He guides me*
*in paths of righteousness*
*for his name's sake.*
Psalm 23:1-3

*The Lord is my shepherd,*
*I shall not be in want.*
*He makes me lie down*
*in green pastures,*
*he leads me beside quiet waters,*
*he restores my soul.*
*He guides me*
*in paths of righteousness*
*for his name's sake.*
Psalm 23:1-3

*The Lord is my shepherd,*
*I shall not be in want.*
*He makes me lie down*
*in green pastures,*
*he leads me beside quiet waters,*
*he restores my soul.*
*He guides me*
*in paths of righteousness*
*for his name's sake.*
Psalm 23:1-3

*The Lord is my shepherd,*
*I shall not be in want.*
*He makes me lie down*
*in green pastures,*
*he leads me beside quiet waters,*
*he restores my soul.*
*He guides me*
*in paths of righteousness*
*for his name's sake.*
Psalm 23:1-3

*The Lord is my shepherd,*
*I shall not be in want.*
*He makes me lie down*
*in green pastures,*
*he leads me beside quiet waters,*
*he restores my soul.*
*He guides me*
*in paths of righteousness*
*for his name's sake.*
Psalm 23:1-3

## Week 10 Memory Verse

| | |
|---|---|
| *A generous man will prosper; he who refreshes others will himself be refreshed.* Proverbs 11:25 | *A generous man will prosper; he who refreshes others will himself be refreshed.* Proverbs 11:25 |
| *A generous man will prosper; he who refreshes others will himself be refreshed.* Proverbs 11:25 | *A generous man will prosper; he who refreshes others will himself be refreshed.* Proverbs 11:25 |
| *A generous man will prosper; he who refreshes others will himself be refreshed.* Proverbs 11:25 | *A generous man will prosper; he who refreshes others will himself be refreshed.* Proverbs 11:25 |

# About the Author

Also post-abortive, Sheila Luck has been on a personal journey of healing and growth for over thirty years, a journey made possible only through God's love and grace. She endeavors to share God's love with others through her books, speaking events, and personal conversations, praying that they too will know his love, and receive his forgiveness for past mistakes and regrettable choices. Sheila hopes that God will use her experiences to save the lives of all pre-born babies. Through emotionally powerful presentation, Sheila supports the work of pregnancy centers and pro-life organizations, emphasizing during fund-raising events the importance of their work. Her books, workshops, and presentations help each reader and participant to become the person that God intended them to be, regardless of their past choices, the impact of other's actions on their lives, or their current circumstances. Finally, Sheila works as a mediator, resolving legal, workplace, church, and family conflicts, all while promoting positive change and lasting relationships. Living in Christ Jesus, Sheila has become an "I Can with I AM" person with attitude, seeking always to make a positive difference.

Please see www.IcanwithIAM.com for more information and like her on Facebook: www.facebook.com/sheilamluck.

**Also by the Author:**

*My Baby's Feet*

Available where books are sold

Amazon link:

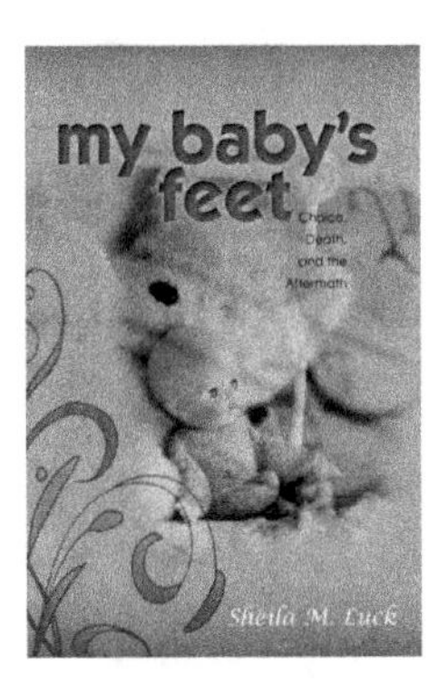


Fearfully and desperately wanting to hide my mistakes and deny the unwanted, but not totally unexpected ramifications of my earlier choices, I chose what seemed to be the easiest answer. I chose death, and then I moved into the aftermath of my choice. I, for a lifetime and beyond, will live in the aftermath of my choice. Although there is recovery, through forgiveness, there are lasting ramifications. No one told me that the ramifications of my choice would last forever. No one told me what my choice would do to my heart. No one told me that my choice was, in fact, a death sentence for my baby.

Are you or someone you know, facing an unwanted pregnancy? Are you wondering if "choice" is the answer, the easiest solution?

After the "choice" comes the aftermath. A living choice not only gives life to a baby, but results in an aftermath of life. Abortion results in an aftermath forever shrouded in death, death of a baby, perhaps death of your own baby. For those struggling with the post abortion aftermath, you and your loved ones can find healing and forgiveness.

This book is for:

- Moms wrestling with choice and an unplanned teen pregnancy
- Loved ones who are seeking resolution after abortion
- Anyone who has had an abortion and wants to know how to feel better.

**Also by the Author:**

*The Upside to Job Loss*

Available where books are sold

Amazon link:

For I know the plans I have for you," declares the Lord, "plans to prosper you and not to harm you, plans to give you hope and a future (Jeremiah 29:11, NIV).

Losing your job creates a new opportunity to discover God's plans for your future. This is great news. Not because you will land that dream job, but because you will discover God's will for your life, and by doing so you will sense genuine fulfillment as He fulfills His plans through you.

This book helps you:

- Identify and define your God-given career and life story.
- Set parameters for a strong, focused job search.
- Become armed with clear employment guidelines.
- Start out your new career on the right foot (or rejuvenate your existing job).

Printed in the USA
CPSIA information can be obtained
at www.ICGtesting.com
LVHW010301050824
787373LV00024B/460